The
NATURAL HISTORY
of
WESTERN MASSACHUSETTS

Written by Stan Freeman
Illustrated by Mike Nasuti

The Connecticut River as seen from Mount Sugarloaf in South Deerfield

Red-winged blackbird   *Black bear*   *Deer fawn*   *Twelve-spotted skimmer*

Hampshire House Publishing Co.
Florence, Mass.

Eastern screech owl chicks

CONTENTS

American toad

Great blue heron

Garter snake

Eastern chipmunk

Red-tailed hawk

Raccoon

Water lily

Roads

North Adams
Greenfield
Pittsfield
Amherst
Northampton
Stockbridge
Holyoke
Chicopee
Westfield
Springfield

Route markers: 2, 8, 8A, 112, 91, 78, 63, 7, 116, 43, 8, 9, 143, 47, 41, 20, 66, 10, 202, 21, 181, 32, 90, 23, 71, 57, 291, 83, 19, 181

Cities and towns

Mileage
0   5   10

Clarksburg
Monroe
Rowe
Heath
Colrain
Leyden
Bernardston
Northfield
Warwick
Williamstown
North Adams
Florida
Charlemont
Shelburne
Greenfield
Gill
Erving
Orange
New Ashford
Adams
Savoy
Hawley
Buckland
Deerfield
Montague
Wendell
Cheshire
Windsor
Plainfield
Ashfield
Conway
Hancock
Lanesborough
Dalton
Whately
New Salem
Pittsfield
Hinsdale
Peru
Cummington
Goshen
Leverett
Shutesbury
Worthington
Hatfield
Pelham
Richmond
Chesterfield
Williamsburg
Hadley
Amherst
Lenox
Washington
Middlefield
Northampton
West Stockbridge
Stockbridge
Lee
Becket
Chester
Huntington
Westhampton
Easthampton
Ware
Alford
Tyringham
Southampton
South Hadley
Granby
Belchertown
Egremont
Great Barrington
Monterey
Otis
Blandford
Montgomery
Holyoke
Chicopee
Ludlow
Palmer
Mount Washington
Russell
West Springfield
Springfield
Wilbraham
Brimfield
Sheffield
New Marlborough
Sandisfield
Tolland
Granville
Southwick
Agawam
Longmeadow
East Longmeadow
Hampden
Monson
Wales
Holland
Westfield

Franklin County
Berkshire County
Hampshire County
Hampden County

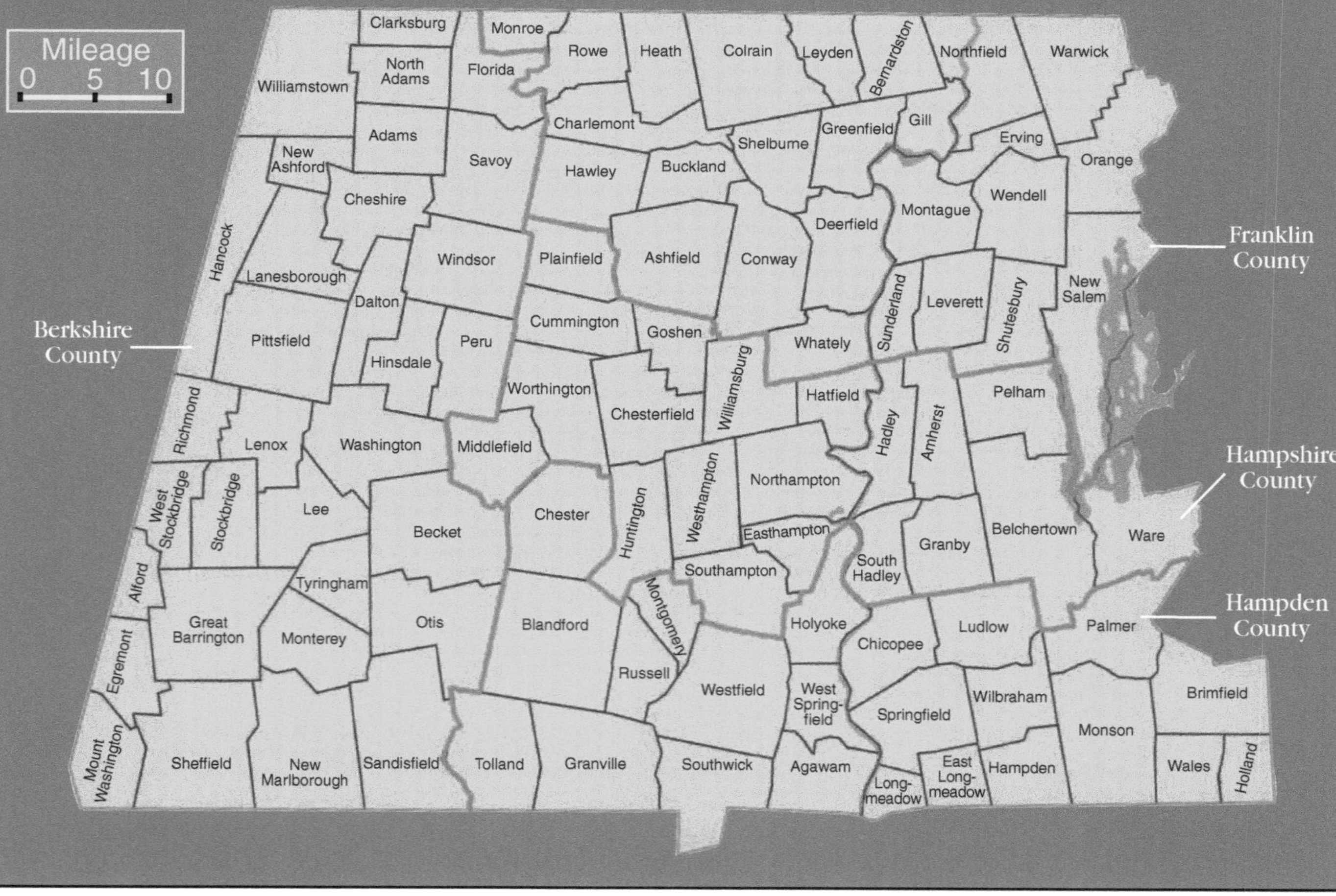

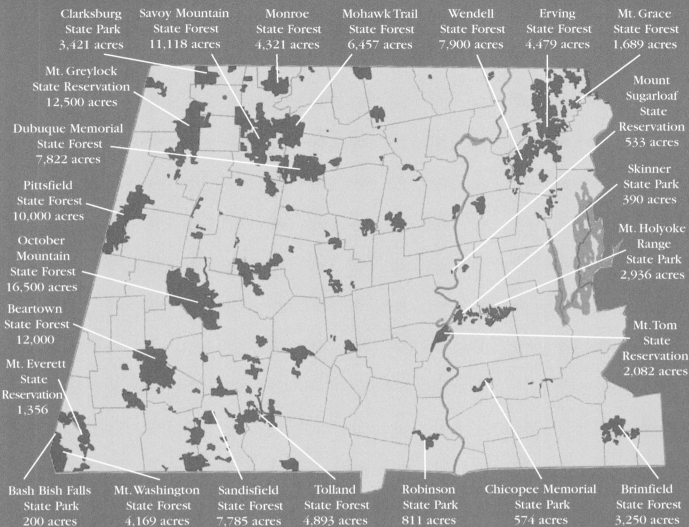

Clarksburg
State Park
3,421 acres

Savoy Mountain
State Forest
11,118 acres

Monroe
State Forest
4,321 acres

Mohawk Trail
State Forest
6,457 acres

Wendell
State Forest
7,900 acres

Erving
State Forest
4,479 acres

Mt. Grace
State Forest
1,689 acres

Mt. Greylock
State Reservation
12,500 acres

Dubuque Memorial
State Forest
7,822 acres

Pittsfield
State Forest
10,000 acres

October
Mountain
State Forest
16,500 acres

Beartown
State Forest
12,000

Mt. Everett
State
Reservation
1,356

Mount
Sugarloaf
State
Reservation
533 acres

Skinner
State Park
390 acres

Mt. Holyoke
Range
State Park
2,936 acres

Mt. Tom
State
Reservation
2,082 acres

Bash Bish Falls
State Park
200 acres

Mt. Washington
State Forest
4,169 acres

Sandisfield
State Forest
7,785 acres

Tolland
State Forest
4,893 acres

Robinson
State Park
811 acres

Chicopee Memorial
State Park
574 acres

Brimfield
State Forest
3,250 acres

Historic population figures

	2000	1980	1960	1940	1920	1900
Berkshire County	134,953	145,110	142,135	122,273	113,033	95,667
Franklin County	71,535	64,317	54,864	49,453	49,361	41,209
Hampden County	456,228	443,018	429,353	332,107	300,305	175,603
Hampshire County	152,251	138,813	103,229	72,461	69,599	58,820
State total	6,349,097	5,737,037	5,148,578	4,316,721	3,852,356	2,805,346

Massachusetts, est. pop., 2015 – 6,794,422

A little more than a century ago, America was not a land where the deer and the antelope played or the buffalo roamed. Populations of these animals and others had been reduced to the point that the survival of some species was very much in doubt.

Similarly, parts of the Northeast were nearly barren of many species of wildlife that had lived here for thousands of years, including black bears, moose and beavers.

The cutting of forests, plowing of meadows, damming of rivers and unrestricted hunting had taken their toll on wildlife.

To halt the decline in animal populations, laws that regulated hunting were established in many states in the early 1900s. This worked well for some animals, such as black bears and white-tailed deer, which gradually returned on their own to areas they had once inhabited.

In the case of animals that did not return on their own, wildlife biologists tried to raise them on game farms for release into the wild, or they captured wild animals in other states for release locally.

However, it was not enough to return these once-native animals to their historic territories. Their habitats – the land and water – also had to be restored. Loss of habitat is the primary reason most species of plants and animals

The bald eagle, once the symbol of vanishing wildlife, is no longer endangered nationally.

become rare or endangered. So thousands of acres of forests were bought to establish state and federal forests, parks and wildlife refuges, and rivers that had been fouled with sewage and trash were gradually cleaned.

If animals were to be restored, they also had to be protected. In 1973, the federal Endangered Species Act was passed, making it a crime to hunt or otherwise harm many species of rare plants and animals. In addition, laws were passed in each state to protect plants or animals that were rare or endangered in that state.

State laws were also passed to protect wetland areas and water bodies, such as ponds, lakes, marshes and rivers. All living things depend on water for survival, and areas where land and water come together, such as the land surrounding a stream or river, are among the richest habitats for plants and animals. Red-winged blackbirds and marsh wrens nest in the cattails of pond edges. Moose feed on vegetation found in swamps and marshes. Muskrats and river otters live much of their lives in water.

Today in Massachusetts, there are nearly 2,150 species of plants and animals considered native to the state. That does not even include the unknown number of invertebrate species – mainly insects.

Massachusetts' rare native species

Protected Massachusetts species as of 2015

Governments have set up a system to classify the health of populations of plants and animals. A species is considered endangered if it is on the verge of extinction in its natural range. It is threatened if it is likely to become endangered in the near future. It is on the federal endangered species list if it is endangered or threatened nationwide. It is on the state list if it is endangered or threatened in Massachusetts even though it may be more common in other states.

	Endangered state list/ federal list	Threatened state list/ federal list
Mammals	11/7	0/0
Birds	11/1	7/1
Reptiles	8/4	5/2
Amphibians	0/0	2/0
Fish[1]	4/1	2/0
Invertebrates[2]	31/2	25/0
Plants	154/2	63/0
Total	219/17	104/3

[1] Includes inland freshwater fish only
[2] Includes butterflies, moths, beetles, dragonflies, crustaceans, mussels, snails, worms and sponges

Federal endangered species list includes these Massachusetts natives:
Humpback whale
Roseate tern
Leatherback seaturtle
Dwarf wedgemussel
Sandplain gerardia
Northeastern bulrush
Shortnose sturgeon

State endangered species list includes:
All Mass. species on the federal list
Peregrine falcon
Barrens tiger beetle
Twilight moth
Short-eared owl
Northern copperhead
Lake chub

Great spangled fritillary, a native species

Black-eyed Susan, a native species

Invaders

Just like many Americans, many plants can trace their roots to foreign soils. There are also animals found in Massachusetts that have ties to other places in America or abroad.

A range of wildflowers, trees, insects, fish, birds and other life forms were brought to the region over the years by gardeners, naturalists, cooks and sportsmen who admired them elsewhere and released them – or allowed them to escape – into the wild here.

Others came as accidental hitchhikers on trucks, cars and airplanes and as stowaways on early sailing ships and ocean freighters. Still others arrived here on their own as part of the natural spread of their species into places where they could survive.

While the vast majority don't harm local ecosystems, a small percentage do. Called "invasives," these aggressive species invade and dominate the landscapes on which they alight, pushing out valued native species. Some naturalists estimate that only about two-thirds of the plants found in the state were here before Europeans arrived. However, only two or three dozen of these late arrivals are considered seriously invasive.

For instance, purple loosestrife was introduced from Europe as a garden flower and eventually escaped into the wild. It has strikingly beautiful flowers, but it can quickly take over a wetland, such as a

Oriental bittersweet, an invasive species introduced from Asia

marsh, pushing out native plant species, some of them important to nesting wetland birds.

European starlings, which were also natives of Europe, were released in Central Park in New York City in the early 1890's by Shakespeare fans who wanted to introduce to America the birds mentioned in the immortal writer's plays. They have since spread from coast to coast and are reducing the populations of some other birds. Starlings nest in tree cavities, taking away nesting sites from other cavity-nesters such as bluebirds, northern flickers and tree swallows.

Oriental bittersweet, introduced from Asia, is a fast-growing vine common to back yards that wraps around shrubs, trees and flowers, forming a thick tangle in which native species perish. In the fall it produces reddish-orange berries.

At least one species of harmful invader, the gypsy moth, was the result of a breeding experiment gone wrong. In 1869, hoping to start a silk business, a Medford, Massachusetts, man tried to cross imported European gypsy moths with silk moths to create a more productive silkworm. The breeding attempt failed, but some of the moth larvae accidentally escaped. Gypsy moths have now spread through most of the East.

In most years, the gypsy moth caterpillars, which feed on tree leaves, defoliate more than a million acres of forests.

European starling, an invasive species introduced from Europe

Purple loosestrife, an invasive species introduced from Europe

Barn owl

From northern cardinals and black-capped chickadees to great horned owls and bald eagles, the skies can seem nearly as populated with birds as the land is with people.

In fact, more populated. It's estimated there may be 20 times as many birds on Earth as humans. Walk through any field or forest in summer and you can easily believe it.

Nearly 330 species of birds can be seen at least once a year in Massachusetts, including almost 225 that nest in the state. In all of North America, more than 800 species of birds have been reported. Worldwide, there may be more than 10,000 species of birds.

While large forests in the state attract their share of birds that seek isolation from humans, such as scarlet tanagers and hermit thrushes, cities and suburbs are home to birds that can easily live around people, such as American goldfinches and mourning doves.

Cedar waxwing

Nearly 150 million years ago, the first birds were appearing on Earth. But they may have looked more like winged lizards than modern birds. Birds, like most creatures, have changed, or evolved, over millions of years to have specialized features that help them survive by giving them an advantage over other living things. For most birds, the most important feature is the ability to fly and to live much of their lives above ground and in the air.

Even among birds, though, different species have evolved to have different features – variations in size, coloring, wing design or body shape. Because of these physical differences, some birds can find food in ways that others can't, or they can live and nest in places where others can't. As a result, more kinds of birds can survive than would be possible if all birds ate the same foods and lived and nested in the same places.

Birds born with a difference that gives them an advantage in finding food, such as a slightly longer beak, or an advantage in escaping predators, such as greater flying speed, are more likely to survive and have young. Therefore, their special features are more likely to be passed along to future generations.

Using this process, called natural selection, woodpeckers developed over millions of years to have strong, sharp beaks, long tongues and sharp claws. They use their claws to grab onto the sides of trees, and they use their beaks to peck nest holes in trees and to dig beneath bark to find insects. They use their long tongues to grab the insects they find.

Herons and egrets developed to have long, thin legs and long, sharp beaks. They use their legs to wade in the shallow water of lakes, streams and ponds. They can stand very still and wait for fish or tadpoles to pass by so that they can spear them with their beaks. To a fish, their thin legs may look like reeds.

Artists of the air

Birds do not merely fly. They also hover, soar and glide. If there are artists of the air, though, it may be the hummingbirds. They have made an art of functional flight.

Hummingbirds evolved to have strong wing muscles for a specific purpose. They can beat their wings very rapidly, on average 55 times each second, to hover at flowers like bumblebees, so that they can use their long beaks and tongues to sip the energy-rich nectar inside flowers.

A female ruby-throated hummingbird

A male ruby-throated hummingbird

In the Northeast, songbirds (a category that includes most backyard birds) usually nest and lay their eggs from April to June. For smaller birds, like the tufted titmouse, white-breasted nuthatch and tree swallow, the eggs take about two weeks to hatch, and the young stay in the nest two to three weeks before they take their first flights.

For larger birds, such as great horned owls and red-tailed hawks, the eggs may take nearly four weeks to hatch, and the young may remain in the nest four to six weeks.

Birds in the wild have varying life spans. Harsh weather, accidents, predators, disease and lack of food can take their toll. Most songbirds live only two to five years.

American robin

However, some larger birds, such as mallards and great blue herons, may live 20 years or more.

Birds are often specialists about food. Many species prefer one type of food. Canada geese like grass, eagles prefer fish, finches look for seeds and warblers like insects. However, most birds will eat more than one kind of food, and some will change their diet as the seasons change.

Generally, the larger a bird is, the faster it can fly. Finches and sparrows can reach top flying speeds of about 20 miles per hour, hawks can fly 30 to 40 miles per hour and geese, when pressed, can fly 60 miles per hour. Peregrine falcons, which hunt from the air, may be capable of the fastest flying speeds,

Backyard birds of Western Massachusetts

Some birds will nest in residential areas. Shown for the birds below is: Nest construction – Average number of eggs per brood – Broods per season – Period during which eggs are laid – Time to hatching – Time to nestlings' first flights

Blue jay

A cup of rootlets, twigs, bark strips and leaves, usually in an evergreen tree 10 to 25 feet off the ground – Four or five eggs – One brood – April 28 to June 18 – About 17 days – About 19 days

Ruby-throated hummingbird

A small cup of plant down, fibers and spider silk built in the fork of a drooping limb, usually 10 to 20 feet off the ground – Two eggs – One or two broods – May 24 to July 22 – About 16 days – About 19 days

Black-capped chickadee

A cavity in a standing dead tree lined with cottony fibers, fur, moss, hair, wool and feathers, usually 4 to 10 feet off the ground – Six to eight eggs – One brood – May 4 to July 12 – About 12 days – About 16 days

American robin

A deep cup made of grasses and weed stalks and shaped with mud in the fork of a tree branch, in shrubs or on a window ledge, usually 5 to 15 feet off the ground – Three or four eggs – Two, rarely three broods – April 12 to July 25 – About 12 days – About 15 days

Downy woodpecker

A cavity in a living or dead tree, usually 20 to 30 feet off the ground – Four or five eggs – One brood – May 20 to June 21 – About 12 days – About 21 days

Northern cardinal

A shallow cup of twigs, grasses, rootlets and vines in dense shrubs or thickets or in an evergreen tree, usually less than 10 feet off the ground – Three or four eggs – Two or three broods – Late April to late June – About 12 days – About 12 days

House sparrow

A cavity lined with grasses, weeds and feathers in a tree, on a building, on a billboard or in a birdhouse, usually 10 to 50 feet off the ground – Four to six eggs – Two or three broods – February to September – About 12 days – About 16 days

Blue jay

Northern cardinal

up to 200 miles per hour. They dive rapidly on their prey, usually other birds in flight, killing them with the impact of the collision.

Feathers are a bird's clothing, keeping it warm in winter and giving it a colorful appearance. A robin may have 3,000 feathers. A tundra swan may have 25,000. However, most birds replace their feathers once or twice a year, a process called molting. The molt may take a month or more to complete.

Some birds, such as male American goldfinches, grow their brightest feathers for the breeding season, when they are trying to attract mates. Then they grow duller-colored feathers for the winter, which makes them less visible to predators.

Since it is most often the male's job to attract a female, in many species, including northern cardinals and American goldfinches, the male has brighter feather coloring than the female. With her plain coloring that often blends in with surrounding vegetation, the female does not draw as much attention to the nest and young.

Eggs
Some bird eggs shown their actual size

For many birds, the color and markings on their eggs have a purpose – to act as camouflage. For birds that build cup nests off the ground, such as cedar waxwings, the base color of their eggs is usually cream or buff and the markings may be streaks or speckles of brown. For birds, such as terns and gulls, that build nests on the ground, where predators are even more of a threat, the camouflage of streaks and speckles can be even more of a necessity. For birds that lay their eggs in darkened holes in trees, such as some owls, the color usually does not matter.

Canada goose

American crow

American robin

Great horned owl

Cedar waxwing

Yellow warbler

Ruby-throated hummingbird

A robin's nest

When a robin's nest shows up unexpectedly on a family's window sill in spring, it instantly becomes a made-to-order field experiment and one of the most compelling entries into the natural sciences that young kids will encounter.

Robins love the worms found in residential lawns, and they are not shy about building their nests near or on a home – or even on a back-yard deck, as in this pictured nest.

In Massachusetts, robins lay their eggs from mid-April to late July in cup-shaped nests made of grasses and weed stalks plastered together with mud. The nests might be built in the fork of tree branches or on a protected flat surface of a home.

With their distinctive sky-blue coloring, the eggs hatch in about 12 days. The fragile hatchlings initially weigh about a fifth of an ounce. As a comparison, that's about the weight of two pennies. But within two weeks, when they are ready to take their first flights, they will weigh nearly 2.5 ounces – about the weight of 12 quarters and about the size of an adult robin. And that means they will have to eat a lot in a short time to gain weight so rapidly.

Robin eggs in a nest

Females do most of the incubation of the eggs, as is the case for most songbirds. But when it comes to feeding the young, both parents do their part.

In the first few days, the parents feed the young swallowed food that they bring back to their mouths, but about day three or four, the nestlings begin eating whole foods, mainly worms and insects.

Studies have found the parents bring food to the nest six to seven times an hour, on average, so that each nestling gets 35 to 40 feedings per day. The parents bring about 200 grams of food to the nest each day, or about seven ounces. That amounts to more than six pounds of wriggly crawly things fed to the young before they leave the nest.

When young robins finally take their first flight about two weeks after hatching, it is usually an awkward trip from the nest to the ground, as they are not yet capable of full flight. The parents may lead them to the protection of shrubs or undergrowth, and they will continue to feed them for several days until they develop the skills to survive on their own.

One day old

Three days old

Two weeks old

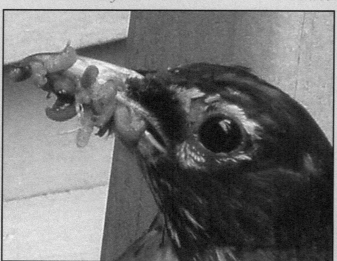

Food for the young

A feeding

Barn swallows build nests of mud and straw that are plastered to building structures.

The stick nests of bald eagles are built high in trees and are used year after year.

Killdeer nests are built on the ground in open areas.

Hummingbird nests are often held together with spider silk.

Nests

Different species of birds build different kinds of nests. One of the most common types is a cup-shaped nest built with grass or twigs in the fork created by two branches of a tree. However, birds also build nests on the ground, atop buildings, on billboards, in barns, on mountain ledges and in holes in trees.

House wrens have been known to build a nest in a discarded shoe, a tin can, a teapot or in the pocket of a shirt hanging on a clothesline.

The largest nests are those of eagles. Some are eight feet across, 15 feet deep, and weigh as much as a small automobile.

The smallest nests are those of hummingbirds. Some are less than an inch across and the eggs are the size of peas.

Pileated woodpeckers peck holes in trees for their nests.

Yellow warblers build nests of milkweed fibers, plant down, hemp and grasses.

The common loon builds its nest by the water using grass, reeds, twigs and rushes. (It visits but generally does not nest in the state.)

Cedar waxwings at their nest

An eastern bluebird entering its nest in a tree hole

A mute swan on its nest in an Easthampton pond

An American redstart checking its chicks

A northern cardinal feeding its young

Songs and calls

The songs and calls of birds are their language. They use these sounds to tell other birds a territory is theirs, to attract a mate and to warn of danger, among other things. Their songs and calls may sound like this:

TUFTED TITMOUSE – "Peter! Peter! Peter!"
MOURNING DOVE – "Coo-ah, coo, coo, coo!"
GRAY CATBIRD – "Meow!"
OVENBIRD – "Teacher, teacher, teacher!"
GREAT HORNED OWL – "Who, who-who-who, who, who!"
EASTERN TOWHEE – "Drink your tea!"
BALTIMORE ORIOLE – "Hew-lee!"
WHITE-THROATED SPARROW – "Poor Sam Peabody, Peabody, Peabody!"
AMERICAN GOLDFINCH – "Potato chip!"
RED-WINGED BLACKBIRD – "Ok-a-lee!"
COMMON YELLOWTHROAT – "Witchity, witchity, witchity, witch!"
BLUE JAY – "Thief! Thief!" or "Jay! Jay!"

American goldfinch

Tufted titmouse

Mourning dove

Great horned owl

Baltimore oriole

Migration

Because northern winters can be harsh and food can be scarce, many birds migrate in the fall to warmer regions in the southern United States and Central and South America. Then they return in the spring. However, some birds stay in Massachusetts through the winter, including northern cardinals, blue jays and crows. Some birds of a species, like the eastern bluebird, will stay in the state through the winter, but most migrate south.

During the migration, birds may travel 200 to 300 miles a day. Some, like hawks and ducks, travel during daylight hours, but most smaller birds travel at night when they are less visible to predators.

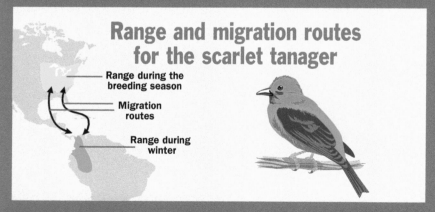

Range and migration routes for the scarlet tanager

Range during the breeding season

Migration routes

Range during winter

Typical migration times in Massachusetts

	Arrival	Departure
Eastern bluebird	Early March	Oct.
Song sparrow	Late March, early April	Sept., Oct.
Eastern meadowlark	Mid-March, early April	Oct.
House wren	Late April, early May	Sept.
Broad-winged hawk	Late April	Mid-Sept.
Yellow warbler	Early May	Late July, early Aug.
Barn swallow	Late April, early May	Mid-Aug.
Baltimore oriole	Early May	Late Aug., early Sept.
Scarlet tanager	Mid-May	Sept.

CHECKLIST
Common birds

Red-winged blackbird
8 in. from tip of beak to tip of tail

☐

Eastern bluebird
6 in.

☐

Northern cardinal
8 in.

M   F

☐

Black-capped chickadee
5 in.

☐

American crow
19 in.

☐

Mourning dove 12 in. ☐

Rock dove (pigeon) 13 in. ☐

House finch 6 in. ☐

Northern flicker 13 in. ☐

American goldfinch 5 in. ☐ M F

Canada goose 38 in. ☐

Common grackle 12 in. ☐

Ring-billed gull 19 in. ☐

Great blue heron 48 in. ☐

Ruby-throated hummingbird 3 in. ☐ M F

Blue jay 12 in. ☐

Dark-eyed junco 6 in. ☐

Belted kingfisher 13 in. ☐

Mallard 23 in. ☐

Northern mockingbird 11 in. ☐

White-breasted nuthatch 6 in. ☐

Baltimore oriole 8 in. ☐

American robin 10 in. ☐

House sparrow 6 in. ☐

Song sparrow 6 in. ☐

White-throated sparrow 7 in. ☐

European starling 8 in. ☐

Tree swallow 6 in. ☐

Tufted titmouse 6 in. ☐

Cedar waxwing 7 in. ☐

Downy woodpecker 6 in. ☐

House wren 5 in. ☐

Woodpeckers
How do these tree-pounding birds avoid headaches?

It's like banging your head against a brick wall – exactly like it.

Woodpeckers have certainly earned their name. They peck on trees to create nesting holes, to find insects beneath the bark and to communicate with other woodpeckers. But the loud, rapid rat-a-tat-tat of of a woodpecker is produced with such force that it would likely cause death or severe brain damage in any other living thing that tried it.

Indeed, the force with which these head-banging birds strike a tree is at least 13 times more than the force of a car crash that would kill or severely injure the average man, woman or child, studies have found. Yet, they can peck 20 times a second and more than 12,000 times a day without apparent damage.

How do they survive the tremendous blows to their head? It's because their skulls and bodies have evolved to have features that cushion the impact and protect the brain.

It's estimated that 99.7 percent of the force of the striking blow of the beak is absorbed by the body, not the brain. And the energy that is absorbed by the brain is mainly turned to heat. That's one reason why a woodpecker tends to peck in short bursts. When it stops, the brain's temperature has a chance to return closer to normal.

When a woodpecker is pecking, it moves around the posi-

Northern flicker

tion of its head to prevent any one spot of their brain from getting too much of a pounding. And in critical places, the bones of the skull have a "spongy" structure, which allows them to absorb much of the energy of the peck before it reaches the brain. Also, unlike humans, whose brains are loosely packed in their skulls, a woodpecker's brain is tightly packed so that there is little space between the brain and skull, which means the brain does not rattle around during a peck's impact.

One feature of a woodpecker's skull is especially helpful. There is a bone, called the hyoid bone, that wraps around its brain, acting like a seat belt to hold it in place during pecking. And its design diverts much of the energy of the pecking away from the brain.

As for the beak of a woodpecker, it is very sharp and the pecking drives it into the wood rather than bluntly hammering it. Also, the upper beak is slightly longer than the lower beak, which means the upper beak absorbs more of the force of a peck. That energy travels along the upper beak to where it encounters the hyoid bone, which sends the force away from the brain.

Two other features also help woodpeckers survive their hammering. Thick neck muscles absorb much of the energy of the pecking, and a third inner eyelid closes on impact, preventing the bird's eyeballs from popping out of its head as it noisily pounds away on a tree.

Common woodpeckers

Downy woodpecker
6 inches, tip of the beak to end of the tail

Yellow-bellied sapsucker
8 inches

Hairy woodpecker
10 inches
(Looks very much like the downy but has a proportionately longer bill)

Red-bellied woodpecker
11 inches

Northern flicker
12 inches
(Often seen hunting ants on the ground)

Pileated woodpecker
18 inches

Hairy woodpecker

Yellow-bellied sapsucker

Red-bellied woodpecker

Pileated woodpecker

Downy woodpecker

Raptors

Raptors are the rulers of the skies. Eagles, hawks, falcons, owls and other birds of prey (as raptors are also called) have features that are standards of excellence in the animal world. Consider the sharp eyes of an eagle, the keen hearing of an owl or the breathtaking speed of a diving falcon. Throughout the Northeast, the populations of many species of these raptors are soaring. It has become common now to see a red-tailed hawk sitting high on a roadside tree or an American kestrel perched on a telephone wire.

In the 1960s, though, some species of raptors were headed for extinction. A widely used chemical pesticide, DDT, caused them to lay eggs with no shells or shells so thin that they broke. DDT was banned in 1972, and almost immediately, populations of birds of prey began to recover.

In 1963, there were only 487 known pairs of nesting eagles in the lower 48 states. Today, there are nearly 10,000 pairs, including about 30 active pairs in Massachusetts.

A 2013 survey found eight active eagle nests along the Connecticut River in the state and six near the shores of Quabbin Reservoir.

Peregrine falcons, whose population was similarly reduced, also recovered. Since 1989, a pair has nested in many years on a 21st floor window ledge of a downtown Springfield office building.

Many raptors have also been helped by changes in how land is used. A little more than a century ago, farm fields covered much of the Northeast, but many of those farms have been abandoned, and the fields have grown back to forests.

Today, the region has a rich mixture of landscapes – patches of forests that are alongside patches of meadows, farm fields or residential neighborhoods. And this change has helped many species, especially those that like to perch in trees on the edges of forests and hunt small animals in open areas, such as Cooper's hawks and red-tailed hawks.

However, a few species have been hurt by the changes, especially barn owls and northern harriers, which prefer farms and fields.

Great horned owl

Red-tailed hawk nest on the University of Massachusetts campus in Amherst

American kestrel

Broad-winged hawk

Barn owl

Osprey

Snowy owl

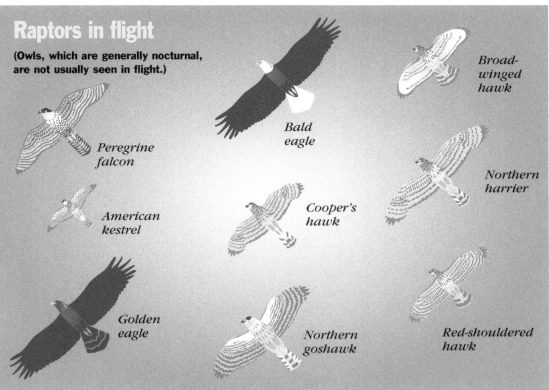

Raptors in flight

(Owls, which are generally nocturnal, are not usually seen in flight.)

Peregrine falcon

Bald eagle

Broad-winged hawk

American kestrel

Cooper's hawk

Northern harrier

Golden eagle

Northern goshawk

Red-shouldered hawk

Bald eagle chick in its nest on the Connecticut River in West Springfield

Chesterfield Gorge in Chesterfield

5–6 in.
long

Moose disappeared from Massachusetts in the early 1700s, save for the occasional wandering migrant from states to the north where they were still common, such as Maine. Unregulated hunting and the clearing of forests to create farms drove them out of Massachusetts.

As recently as the 1970s, sighting a moose in the commonwealth was still a rarity. Now, though, there is the potential to see moose in almost any Western Massachusetts community. Once considered too warm for cold-loving moose to colonize, the state is now home to as many as 1,200 of these majestic mammals.

As harmless as moose may seem, though, they can pose a serious problem for people driving on highways. Moose are so large (males can weigh more than a half ton and stand six feet at the shoulder) that they usually feel no need to flee from danger, whether it's an approaching animal or an oncoming car. Moose often hold their ground, and that can result in serious accidents when a car and a moose collide. Because their impressive weight sits atop long, spindly legs, they may topple right over the hood of a car, sometimes crashing right through the windshield.

Moose are most likely to be seen near dawn and dusk when they are foraging for food. They are most frequently seen in September and October, when males (bulls) are

Moose are often found around swamps and lakes in summer, eating vegetation and submerging in the water to escape insects. In the wild, moose can live up to 20 years.

wandering in search of females (cows) during the breeding season. At that time of year, in areas where moose are found, you might hear the resounding bellows of bulls as they call to potential mates. Females usually produce one calf a year.

A bull's massive rack of antlers, which can be five feet across, is shed each year in winter. The antlers begin to grow in late March and reach their full size by August. Moose are a type of deer and, as with all deer, the females do not grow antlers. Sometimes, when bulls joust, their antlers become locked together and the moose perish.

Moose keep to themselves much of the time, although several may gather in a feeding area. In winter, they feed mainly on twigs. In summer, they add aquatic plants, leaves and grasses to their diets.

Moose

2–3 in. long

Graceful and elegant, deer are animals that a child might imagine in dreams. To see a doe and its fawns grazing in a meadow in the early morning light or an antlered buck nibbling tree seedlings in a sunlit forest is to see something that one does not easily forget.

But white-tailed deer graze in places other than meadows and forests. They graze in farm fields, in vegetable gardens and on ornamental shrubs. They also wander across well-traveled highways from dusk to dawn in search of still more grazing opportunities. And where deer go, Lyme disease, which is carried by deer ticks and which can affect humans, may follow. So not everyone loves to see whitetails.

A century ago, deer were rare in much of the Northeast. Sightings of them were often reported in newspapers. But with the return of the forests and limits on hunting, the deer also returned. By 1967, the size of the state's deer herd was estimated to be 8,000 animals. Today there may be up to 95,000 deer spread across Massachusetts.

In the wild, white-tailed deer may live seven years or more. If food is plentiful, a doe may breed when she is six months old and have a fawn around her first birthday in the spring. In later years, she may have one to three fawns each spring, which means deer populations can grow rapidly.

As with many animals, the males are larger than the females. Bucks usually weigh 100 to 200 pounds, and

White-tailed deer may gather in dense stands of evergreens, called "deer yards," in severe winters with deep snow. Snow depths are usually less there, and deer can browse on the branches. The trees also give them protection from wind, cold temperatures and blowing snow.

does may reach 70 to 150 pounds. Bucks grow antlers each year, usually starting in April, and shed them in winter, late December to February.

There is a saying that when a leaf falls in the forest, an eagle will see it, a bear will smell it and a deer will hear it. Gifted with extremely sharp hearing, white-tailed deer are tough and hardy survivors. They use their hearing and swiftness afoot – they can run at speeds of 35 miles per hour – to avoid the few predators they have, and they can live close to residential neighborhoods while rarely being seen.

Deer prefer areas where there are forests mixed with clearings, wetlands, abandoned pastures or active farms. They are vegetarians, favoring the buds and twigs of young trees in the cold months, and grasses, fresh leaves and nuts, such as acorns, in the warm months.

White-tailed deer

6–7 in. long

What is there about a bear that has such a dramatic effect on people? From affection for panda bears to fear of grizzly bears, human emotions run high at the sight of them. Indeed, to come face-to-face with a bear is perhaps the ultimate wildlife experience of the forest – and increasingly of the suburbs.

There may now be 4,000 black bears roaming Massachusetts. Most are settled west of the Connecticut River. With no major predators except humans, a bear can wander just about anywhere it wants, and many have discovered the food resources of residential areas, including bird feeders and trash cans.

Black bears were just about gone from the state in 1900, pushed out mainly by unregulated hunting and trapping. As recently as 1980, the state's bear population, perhaps 400 animals, was found mainly in forested areas along the Mohawk Trail in northern Franklin and Berkshire counties. As their population has expanded, so has their range, moving south and east in the state.

Black bears have long suffered from a public relations problem created by the larger, more aggressive grizzly bears, which are not found in the eastern United States. The difference is that eastern black bears rarely attack human beings. Usually, they are fairly docile creatures and won't attack unless they are defending a cub or have been surprised.

Black bears can live 25 years or more. Males typically weigh 130 to 500 pounds, while females may weigh 100 to 300 pounds.

Bears eat little meat, focusing instead on plant matter that is available through the seasons, from skunk cabbage and grasses in the spring to apples and acorns in the fall,

Black bears are not true hibernators. While a bear's heart rate drops dramatically during the winter dormancy, its temperature does not. Female bears give birth to young in the den, typically in January, so a high body temperature is necessary for them to care for the young.

when they are trying to fatten up for their winter sleep. However, their taste for honey is well known. Black bears have an extraordinary sense of smell that they use to locate food and detect danger.

In Massachusetts, bears are usually active in daytime during the spring and fall, but they are more active during the hours around dawn and dusk in summer.

Females give birth during their winter dormancy every other year, usually having two to four cubs.

Black bear

Black bear raiding a bird feeder in Florence

*Red fox
track,
2 in. long*

To see a red fox in the wild is memorable. True to its reputation, a fox is as sly as ... well, a fox. Very secretive, it can live close to residential areas but almost never be seen. It's also an impressive looking animal with its silky red fur and sharp features.

Red foxes are not animals primarily of the deep forest. They prefer farmland or forest edges. The suburbs, with its mix of fields and small wood lots, can also be an excellent habitat for them.

By contrast, gray foxes, which are less common in Massachusetts, usually live in forested or brushy areas.

Both red and gray foxes are smaller than most people expect, usually weighing just seven to 14 pounds, about as much as a large house cat. They have varied diets, eating what animals and plants are available through the seasons, including rabbits, rodents, birds, insects, snakes, turtles, apples and berries.

Gray fox

Red foxes are active year-round. In winter, they hunt small rodents, such as voles and mice, which move about in tunnels under the snow. A red fox's ears are very sensitive to low sounds, and it will sit on deep snow, listening for prey moving beneath it, then pounce, digging frantically, to capture the animal.

Very often, foxes will not eat what they capture, especially if they are full. Instead, they will bury the prey for a later meal.

Vixens, or female foxes, bear their young in dens in late March or early April. They may have four to seven kits, which begin to spend time outside the den in early May. By late summer, the young will leave their parents' care permanently.

Unlike red foxes, gray foxes, which have sharp claws, will climb trees to reach potential food, such as bird eggs. They will also scamper up a tree to escape danger. While a red fox den is nearly always underground, a gray fox will sometimes den off the ground in a hollow tree.

Red and gray foxes are found throughout the state, except on Martha's Vineyard and Nantucket.

Red fox

Eastern coyote track, 2.5 in. long

"Ravenous cruell creatures." That was the description our Colonial ancestors gave of wolves.

Because of repeated attacks on their livestock, European settlers offered bounties for these stealthy predators, and gradually a predator that had been at the top of the food chain in the Northeast was eliminated. In 1805, two wolves caught roaming between Amherst and Montague were perhaps the last of their breed to be killed in the state.

It has long been assumed as fact that wolves no longer reside in the state. However, it now seems that assumption has been wrong – well, half wrong.

The wolf may again be on the prowl in Massachusetts in the form of the eastern coyote. Genetic tests of tissue samples of coyotes in the Northeast have found evidence of wolf genes in the mix, sometimes to the point that the animals tested were more wolf than coyote.

Today, there are two wolves native to North America – the gray wolf, also called the timber wolf, which is found mainly in Canada, and the smaller, and more rare, red wolf. Only a few hundred red wolves remain and they live mainly in captivity in zoos and breeding facilities.

The eastern wolf, found mainly in eastern Canada, was thought to be a subspecies of gray wolf. However, some now believe it too may be a distinct species of wolf.

There had long been the suspicion that the eastern coyote had some wolf in it. It was known that coyotes,

Eastern coyote

which were not found east of the Mississippi River before 1900, migrated up into Canada from the western United States, crossed north of the Great Lakes and appeared in Massachusetts in the 1950s. However, this newly arrived coyote in the Northeast was noticeably larger than the coyote of the West. Did coyotes and wolves interbreed in Canada?

It took the rise of biotechnology and genetic analysis in the 1990s to confirm the suspicions. Indeed, researchers found wolf genes in eastern coyotes – mainly those of the eastern and gray wolves.

It is known that canids – members of the family that includes wolves, coyotes, foxes and dogs – will interbreed when mating partners of their own kind become scarce. And when so many wolves were killed when the continent was being colonized, wolfs apparently did mate with coyotes, producing our eastern coyote.

All this has thrown views of North America's "wild dogs" – wolves and coyotes – into a state of confusion. Some say the eastern coyote should more properly be called something else, perhaps even a new type of wolf.

Eastern coyotes are now found throughout the state, except on Martha's Vineyard and Nantucket.

Eastern coyote
Length: 4-5 ft.
(nose to tail)
Weight: 43 lbs.
(average male)

Western coyote
Length: 3.5-4.5 ft.
(nose to tail)
Weight: 33 lbs.
(average male)

Gray wolf
Length: 5-6 ft.
(nose to tail)
Weight: 80 lbs.
(average male)

Red wolf
Length: 4.5-5.5 ft.
(nose to tail)
Weight: 65 lbs.
(average male)

Eastern coyotes

The eastern coyote can look a lot like a German shepherd dog. However, coyotes are usually smaller and leaner. Also, a coyote's tail will usually be carried lower to the ground than that of a shepherd.

Eastern coyotes usually weigh 30 to 50 pounds, more than western coyotes. They are often grayish tan in color, but their coats can also be blond, red or even charcoal black. Strong swimmers, good jumpers (up to 15 feet) and swift runners (speeds of nearly 40 miles per hour have been observed), Eastern coyotes are also able hunters, with superior sight, smell and hearing.

Coyotes, which are most active from dusk to dawn, are usually no threat to humans. They are expert scavengers, eating almost anything edible from the bottom of the food chain to the top – from berries, fruits and insects to mice, rabbits and, yes, even the occasional house cat.

Eastern coyotes hunt alone, in mated pairs or in family groups. Coyotes are famous for their howls in the night, a form of communication for them. They will even howl in response to sirens, car alarms and train whistles. But often, the howling is meant to tell non-family members to stay out of the territory.

5 in. long

Beavers are nature's engineers, creating dams and lodges that are marvels of construction. However, their dense, water-resistant fur has always been highly prized for clothing, and uncontrolled trapping during Colonial times eliminated beavers from much of the Northeast. Virtually trapped out of Massachusetts by the late 1700s, beavers have slowly moved back into most parts of the state, helped by a regulated trapping season and wildlife restoration programs. However, they are still uncommon in southeastern Massachusetts, and they are absent from Cape Cod, Martha's Vineyard and Nantucket.

In 1928, beavers were discovered in West Stockbridge, the first recorded occurrence of any beavers in the state since 1750. By 1946, there were an estimated 300 beavers in 45 colonies in Massachusetts, all located west of the Connecticut River.

But as the beaver population grows and spreads, these industrious animals often compete for space in residential areas. Having a beaver pond in the neighborhood is a delight to many people, but a nuisance to others as the ponds can sometimes flood back yards, roads and wells.

From their protruding, orange-tinted, buck teeth to the end of their paddlelike tails, adult beavers are two to three feet long, and they can weigh 30 to 70 pounds. They use their broad, flat tails as rudders when they swim, but they also use them to warn other beavers of danger by loudly slapping them on the water's surface. A beaver can stay submerged in water for up to 15 minutes.

Beavers use trees as their prime building material, and they also feed on the bark. Their favorite trees include poplars, birches, maples, willows and alders. They usually fell trees at night and are able to gnaw their way through a

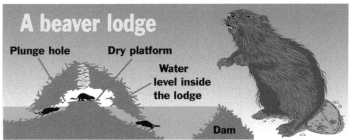

A beaver lodge
Plunge hole   Dry platform
Water level inside the lodge
Dam

willow that is five inches in diameter in just a few minutes.

Beavers dam streams to create ponds. They spend much of their lives in water, which protects them from predators. They begin by laying branches and twigs across a stream that may be in a slight valley. Then they pack down this material with mud, extending the dam's width and height as they go.

Their trademark lodge can sit near the shore of a pond or right in the middle, surrounded by water. The roof of the lodge is made of twigs and mud. Inside, it has a dry platform just above the water line with one or two plunge holes for an entrance and exit. For protection, beavers almost always work on dams and lodges at night.

In winter, beavers do not hibernate. They remain awake in the lodge, occasionally going out beneath the ice to retrieve tree branches they've stored in the water nearby for a meal. A family of beavers can eat a ton of bark in winter. Beavers take a mate for life. The young, called kits, are born in May or June and will take to the water within hours.

Once they dam a stream, a family of beavers typically stays in that location five or six years, expanding the system of dams and ponds as the family grows. Several generations of the family can make up the colony.

A beaver lodge

A beaver and a freshly gnawed tree

A beaver's strong orange teeth

1.5 in. long

A blood-curdling scream deep in the night brings frantic calls to local police, but no evidence of any kind of crime is found.

The mystery is no mystery to wildlife biologists. They know that in the spring what may sound like a crime of passion is in many cases a bobcat in the heat of passion during mating. Its scream is similar in pitch to that of a human female.

Sly. Secretive. Solitary. Bobcats are a rare sight even in areas where they might be common. Bobcats may look like house cats who have done some serious weight training, but the two have quite different lineages. House cats are descended from the first cats domesticated about 4,000 years ago, when Egyptians took the African wild cat and tamed it to keep granaries free of rodents. Later, they were bred as pets.

Bobcats, on the other hand, derive from the Eurasian lynx that took the opportunity perhaps two million years ago to migrate from Asia to North America across a periodic land bridge that emerged across the Bering Strait during ice ages. The lynx learned to live in snow-free regions of the continent, including Mexico, and eventually evolved into the more muscular bobcat.

Visually, what distinguishes the bobcat from most house cats is its tail. It's a bobbed, or shortened, version, about six inches long, of what one usually sees on the house cat. The way a bobcat carries itself can also tell you this is not a house cat on the prowl. They have a certain confidence, a sense that they are only predator and not prey

The size of the bobcat population in Massachusetts is unknown. Since they are secretive, they are difficult to survey. However, bobcats have a home range in winter of about 10 to 20 square miles, so that may limit how many can live in an area.

Typically, bobcats are 28 to 47 inches long and weigh 15 to 35 pounds. Females have one litter per year of one to four kittens born in spring. The young are raised entirely by the female as the male takes no part in family life.

Bobcats, which live about 12 years on average in the wild, are active before dusk to just after dawn in summer and also during the daytime in winter. Their dens

Bobcats will capture an animal, such as a young or sick deer, in winter and eat until they are full. Then they will cover the carcass with snow to return to later for a meal.

are usually formed in a rock crevice, cave, brush pile or hollow log and then lined with dried grass, leaves, moss, and other soft vegetation. They are active throughout the year.

Their diet consists of rabbits and other small mammals in summer, and in winter, snowshoe hares, if they can find them, and occasionally sick or weakened deer. For younger bobcats, starvation is the number one killer.

Bobcat

A bull moose at rest

Black bear cubs explore a tree in Northampton

A bobcat mother and her kitten out for a walk

A raccoon hunts in a wetland

A young porcupine practices climbing

Red fox kits emerge from their den

3-4 in. long

The New England cottontail sustained the lives of Native Americans and early European settlers by providing both meat for eating and fur for warm clothing. But this once abundant rabbit has apparently gone extinct in much of Western Massachusetts and all of the Connecticut River Valley in the state.

However, it's likely that few people have noticed its loss. That's because it's been replaced in the region's forests and thickets by a virtual twin, the Eastern cottontail.

A common resident as recently as 1960 of all of southern New England and much of the northern region, the New England cottontail is now found in only small numbers and isolated pockets in the six states. It has not been seen in the valley for more than a decade.

What caused the general disappearance of Sylvilagus transitionalis, the New England cottontail? One would think it was the appearance of Sylvilagus floridanus, the larger, more aggressive eastern cottontail, imported into the region from the Midwest for hunting.

But the explanation is not that simple.

New England has three resident rabbits – the two cottontails and the snowshoe hare. Snowshoe hares are dark brown in summer, but they turn white in winter, which camouflages them in the snow. Besides their white coat, what distinguishes them is their large, wide back feet, useful for bounding through snow as if on snowshoes.

For most people, the two cottontails would be tough to tell apart. The main difference is that about half of eastern cottontails have a white spot on the forehead. New England cottontails never do. There is also a difference in the ears. Those of the New England cottontail are slightly shorter than those of the eastern. In addition, the New England cottontail has a black spot between its ears, and the ears themselves have a thin black line of fur along the outer edge, features missing from the eastern about half the time.

The eastern is also the larger of the two cottontails, averaging two to four pounds to the New England cottontail's 1.5 to three pounds.

The eastern cottontail was

Eastern cottontail

These rabbits are prolific breeders, having three or four litters per year of three to six young. The adults are typically **14** to **18** inches in length and two to four pounds in weight. They are most active from dusk to just after dawn and they eat mainly plant matter, such as grasses and herbs in summer, and bark, twigs and buds in winter. They are active year-round, although they retreat to shelter during harsh winter weather.

introduced into Massachusetts as early as the 1880s on Nantucket. However, to benefit hunters, between 1924 and 1941 the state imported at least 16,200 Eastern cottontails from the Midwest, where they were natives, and released them across the rest of the commonwealth.

Eastern cottontails slowly began to dominate in Massachusetts. A study from 1960-62 found that of more than 500 cottontails collected within a 20-mile radius of Amherst, 62 percent were eastern cottontails and 38 percent were New England cottontails. In a second study from 1991-93 involving 967 cottontails, mostly received from hunters, 96 percent were easterns and four percent were New England cottontails. More recent surveys have found no New England cottontails in the Connecticut River Valley in Massachusetts.

Given the reproductive abilities of both species of cottontails, that there should be any decline in population of either may be surprising to some.

However, studies of the behaviors of the two cottontails found that the eastern was more often willing to move into the open to get food than the New England cottontail, which would generally not venture from the safety of thickets.

Also, in another study, researchers found that because an eastern cottontail's eyes are larger than those of a New England cottontail, it reacted faster to the approach of a predatory owl.

Ultimately, it may be that the eastern cottontail is just better equipped to survive on a New England landscape that is losing its thickets and turning to more open fields, forests and residential neighborhoods.

Snowshoe hare

New England cottontail

Eastern cottontail

Bald eagles, Bengal tigers and giant pandas are all darlings of science and the media, sharing a charisma factor. Bats, along with cockroaches and rats, suffer from a "yuck" factor and are largely shunned.

However, there would be a world of difference in a world without bats. They eat an amazing number of insects, primarily moths and beetles. It's estimated that a single bat can eat 600 insects in an hour (although contrary to popular belief, mosquitoes are not a principal part of a bat's diet).

We may soon experience a world without bats, though. In Massachusetts and elsewhere bats are dying in high numbers. A fungus, called white-nose syndrome, is threatening bats throughout the eastern United States and Canada, causing devastating losses of their populations.

Once the most common bat in the United States, the little brown bat is now being considered for the endangered species list. It's estimated that nearly 95 percent of little brown bats in the eastern half of the country have died from white-nose syndrome.

First identified in New York in 2006, the disease has spread rapidly. As of 2014, it had been detected in bats in 25 states in the eastern United States and in five Canadian provinces. Some scientists believe the little brown bat may vanish from the country entirely in a little more than a decade.

Often described as "flying mice," bats are, in fact, not rodents. They are mammals. There are nine species of bats that are native to Massachusetts, including the two most common, the little and big brown bats. The little brown bat has about a 10-inch wingspan while the big brown bat measures 13 inches wing tip to wing tip. Typically, a little brown bat weighs just a quarter of an ounce, about the weight of a quarter, compared to two-thirds of an ounce for the big brown bat.

Prior to the current bat illness, the little brown bat was the species most people crossed paths with, as it has a habit of slipping into houses through impossibly small gaps and holes. In summer, during the day. the little brown may roost, or rest, in attics, behind window shutters and in other dark, hot, sheltered places.

While bats can be carriers of rabies, they are not usually infected. But health officials warn people never to handle

A bat's radar

Bats have fairly good eyesight, but in the dark, eyes have little value. So bats have evolved to have a kind of radar that depends on high-frequency sounds that humans can't hear. As a bat flies, it emits short cries at this frequency. The waves of sound go out and when they hit something solid, such as a tree branch or a flying insect, they bounce off the object and return to the bat, which picks up the returning sound with its ears. The bat's brain analyzes the time the sound wave took to return, whether it is an irregular signal and what its pitch is to determine how far ahead the object is. These things will tell it whether it is a flying insect, and whether or not it is moving toward the bat or away from it. For instance, the fluttering wings of a moth might produce a fluttering echo wave.

Echo wave

a bat with bare hands and to treat any bat flying in the living quarters of a home as if it has rabies. The best method to get rid of it is to open a window and leave the room.

The bats in Massachusetts have two main wintering strategies. The hoary, red and silver-haired bats migrate south with the birds. All of the others go to mines and caves in September and October to hibernate.

Why mines and caves? In winter, the temperature and humidity in these chambers can be considerably higher than conditions outside. During hibernation for little brown bats, breathing slows to one breath every five minutes and body temperature drops until it is only slightly higher than the surrounding air. Groups of them form tight clusters, hanging from the ceiling by their feet.

It is in these hibernating chambers that white-nose syndrome spreads within these large groups of sleeping bats, killing most of the infected bats through the winter. The largest bat hibernation site in this state was in Chester, where nearly 10,000 bats were counted in late 2007. However by the end of the next winter, in early 2009, only 14 living bats were counted there.

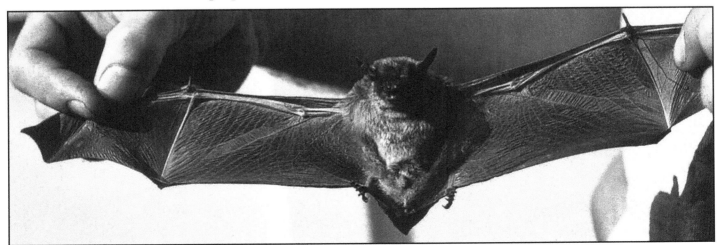

Little brown bat

1.5 in. long

"Once bitten, twice shy" certainly applies to those who have encountered striped skunks. Sprayed just once with a striped skunk's unmistakable scent, and you will never want to repeat the experience.

Skunks have one of the more effective defenses against predators on the planet. Their scent spray, which can travel 15 feet in the air if the wind is right, is so strong it can temporarily blind a victim.

Their bold coloring – black with a white stripe running down their back – makes the lesson that much more unforgettable. "If you see another animal that looks like this, stay clear," the distinctive colors seem to say.

Skunks, which usually weigh three to 12 pounds, eat almost anything, including snails, small rodents, birds' eggs, fruit, grain, nuts, berries and garbage.

Typically, they are nocturnal animals, and a sign one has been in your yard is shallow holes dug in the ground. A skunk was likely digging for grubs or worms during the night.

Skunks are usually active earlier in the spring than other mammals. They might spend the winter under a stump, in a stone wall, in an abandoned burrow or even under a house. But in mid-February the breeding season starts. Males may emerge from their dens and travel in search of females even when there is snow on the ground. This is a time of year when wandering males often cross paths with dogs, coyotes and other non-hibernating species. For many people, the pungent odor that results from such a

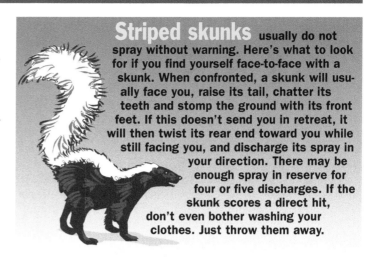

Striped skunks usually do not spray without warning. Here's what to look for if you find yourself face-to-face with a skunk. When confronted, a skunk will usually face you, raise its tail, chatter its teeth and stomp the ground with its front feet. If this doesn't send you in retreat, it will then twist its rear end toward you while still facing you, and discharge its spray in your direction. There may be enough spray in reserve for four or five discharges. If the skunk scores a direct hit, don't even bother washing your clothes. Just throw them away.

meeting is one of the first signs that spring is on the way.

The scent itself is composed of a compound containing sulfur that is secreted by the anal glands. In fact, skunks can be relatively gentle animals and typically will not discharge their scent except as a last resort.

Home remedies to remove the scent from skunk-doused pets often mention a bath in tomato juice, beer or vinegar. But studies have found a more effective mixture is one quart of three percent hydrogen peroxide (which can be obtained from a drug store), a quarter cup of baking soda (sodium bicarbonate) and a teaspoon of liquid detergent. This mixture chemically neutralizes the scent rather than just covering it up.

Striped skunk

Gray squirrel track, 2.5 in. long

The squirrel is one of nature's bankers, wisely putting away resources for the future. Each fall, eastern gray squirrels go about collecting nuts (their favorite food) and burying them one by one for the time when the snow falls and their sources of food disappear.

When winter arrives, they can find their stores, or caches, of acorns and other nuts beneath a foot of snow, not by remembering where they buried them but by smelling them.

Squirrels are rodents, as are chipmunks, woodchucks, beavers and mice. Most rodents hoard or store food to some extent.

In Western Massachusetts, eastern gray squirrels are the squirrels most commonly seen by people. With their quickness and ability to move acrobatically through the treetops, gray squirrels live easily around people and can thrive in residential areas with trees.

Red squirrels are common in many areas with evergreen trees, including residential neighborhoods. But northern and southern flying squirrels, which are also native to the state, are usually found in more remote forested areas.

Gray squirrels may have two litters each year, usually of two to four young per litter. One litter may be born in March and another in July or August. The spring litter is born in a tree den, which is a hollow cavity in a live tree also used during winter for shelter. The summer litter may be born in a large nest built high in a tree using leaves and sticks.

Southern flying squirrel

Flying squirrels

don't actually fly and they don't have wings. They spread open flaps of loose skin between their front and rear legs and glide through the air. Glides of up to 50 yards have been observed.

Occasionally, one may see a black squirrel. It is actually a gray squirrel with a genetic mutation, a trait that can be passed on to offspring. There is a particularly large population of black squirrels in Hampden County believed to be related to several pairs of black squirrels brought from Michigan and released in Stanley Park in Westfield in 1948.

From its nose to the tip of its tail, the gray squirrel is typically 18 to 20 inches long, while the red squirrel is 12 to 14 inches long and the two flying squirrels are nine to 11 inches in length.

Squirrels use their long bushy tails for shade, warmth, protection from rain and snow, balance when climbing and communication with other squirrels. A flying squirrel will also use its tail as a brake and rudder in flight.

Although squirrels may stay in their dens for several days at a time when the weather is harsh in winter, they are active throughout the year.

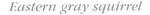
Eastern gray squirrel

Red squirrel

Yes, there are moose and bears and deer in the woods, but it is the small critters that really populate the great outdoors.

In a square mile of good habitat, there might be a few red foxes, a few dozen striped skunks, a few hundred eastern chipmunks and a few thousand short-tailed shrews. That's not to mention the brown bats, red squirrels, gray foxes, beavers, porcupines, cottontails, weasels, coyotes, woodchucks, otters, fishers, bobcats, muskrats, rabbits, voles, mice, minks and moles.

But if there are that many mammals out there, why do we see so few? The reason is that many species are secretive and have habits that help them avoid predators (and human beings). For instance, many are nocturnal – active mainly at night. They sleep and rest in hidden places by day but then go out foraging for food once the sun goes down.

With so many animals sharing the same land, many have evolved to be specialists in where they live and what they eat so that they can survive despite the competition.

Muskrats, beavers and river otters spend much of their life in water. Shrews, moles and voles spend much of their life underground or under the cover of thick grasses or leaves. Squirrels and porcupines spend most of their time in trees. And bats fly.

Porcupines, rabbits and woodchucks are vegetarians. Moles eat worms and ground insects. Bats eat flying insects. Skunks, raccoons and opossums will eat almost anything that can be eaten, including garbage.

Even among mammals, though, there are predators and prey, roles that are often determined by size. The shrews, mice, voles and moles tend to be the prey, while the foxes, coyotes and

Raccoon

bobcats are often the predators.

When approached by a predator, prey animals will use their specialized defenses. The opossum can act as if it's dead. The eastern cottontail can leap 15 feet. Snowshoe hares, which turn white in winter and blend with the snow, can run 27 miles per hour. Striped skunks can spray a fluid that smells terrible and can cause temporary blindness. Porcupines can protect themselves with their coat of sharp quills – as many as 30,000 needlelike spines.

In winter, many mammals either hibernate or become inactive in their dens or burrows. But some, such as coyotes and foxes, are active throughout the year.

It is not just the deep woods and rural meadows that are home to so many mammals. Even urban and suburban neighborhoods can be teeming with wild animals, and not just mammals. Many snakes, birds and insects also call this kind of habitat home.

Because many mammals, such as opossums and skunks, are nocturnal, you rarely see them in residential areas. But they're there. Ask any policeman who drives a cruiser on the midnight to dawn shift.

In fact, when an area is transformed from a rural to a residential landscape, some animals find life easier. They learn to adapt their diet to the new opportunities these neighborhoods can offer, such as bird feeders, vegetable gardens, trash cans, and healthy lawns and shrubs.

Many animals, such as squirrels, chipmunks and a variety of birds, live comfortably with people and are often in sight. Other animals, including garter snakes and woodchucks, live easily among people but prefer to stay out of sight as much as possible.

Porcupine

River otter

Opossum

Woodchuck (groundhog)

Muskrat

Chipmunk

River otter

35 to 54 in. – 12 to 20 lbs. – One litter per year of two to four young born March or April – Active mainly from dusk to after dawn, but can be active any time of day – Eats primarily fish, but also frogs, turtles and aquatic insects – Dens in a rock crevice, under a fallen tree, in an abandoned beaver lodge or muskrat house or in thickets beside water – Active throughout the year

3 in. wide

Porcupine

24 to 30 in. – 8 to 20 lbs. – One litter per year of one young born April to June – Active mainly at night – A strict vegetarian, it eats grasses, twigs, buds and bark – Most den in winter in rocky fissures, hollow trees and logs or vacant buildings, such as sheds, but they may emerge to feed during the day – Active throughout the year

3 in. long

Muskrat

2 in. long

19 to 25 in. (half its length is its tail) – 1 to 4 lbs. – Two to four litters per year of three to eight young born April to September – Active mainly at night, but may be seen during the day – Eats mainly aquatic plants, such as cattails and pond weeds – Constructs a lodge of weeds on water or digs a den in a stream bank – Active throughout the year

Chipmunk

1 in. long

8 to 10 in. – 2 to 5 oz. – One litter per year of three to five young born in April or May – Active all times of day – Eats mainly seeds, fruits, nuts and insects – Dens underground in a series of tunnels – Hibernates in winter, but may become active for short periods

Opossum

2.5 in. wide

26 to 35 in. – 5 to 9 lbs. – One or two litters per year usually of six to nine young, but sometimes as many as 20, born February to July – Active mainly at night – Eats nearly anything, including insects, fruits, nuts, carrion and garbage – Dens in an abandoned burrow, tree cavity, brush pile or thicket – Becomes less active in winter, but does not hibernate

Raccoon

3.5 in. long

22 to 34 in. – 15 to 25 lbs. – One litter per year of three to seven young born April or May – Active mainly at night – Eats everything from small animals and birds to grains and garbage – Dens in a ground cavity, hollow tree, hollow log, pile of rubbish, attic or chimney – Spends winters in its den, but does not hibernate

2 in. long

Woodchuck

19 to 27 in. – 4 to 14 lbs. – One litter per year of four to six young born early April to mid-May – Active by day, especially in the early morning and late afternoon – Eats mainly plants, such as clover and grasses – Dens in a series of underground tunnels ending in a chamber with a grass nest – Hibernates in winter

Roadkill is one of those grisly facts of life.

But to many naturalists, what lies in repose by the roadside can be a source of valuable information if not general fascination. For instance, why do some animals regularly end up as highway fatalities and others do not? As agile as squirrels are, why are they so often victimized? And how is it that fragile little sparrows, which spend so much time down on the roadway, don't even make the list of top 10 road-killed birds (yes, there is such a list), yet the more reclusive gray catbird is right up there among the leaders?

It is unfortunate, but the carnage on the nation's highways is breathtaking. By some estimates, as many as a million animals meet their demise in traffic daily. It may be moose in Maine, white-tailed deer in Pennsylvania, armadillos in Arizona, rattlesnakes in Texas or whiptail lizards in New Mexico.

One survey by a Massachusetts naturalist chronicled roadkill, some 4,000 dead animals, the researcher spotted along the state's highways from 1985 to 1991. To no one's surprise, gray squirrels topped the list. Among birds, pigeons, which often nest beneath overpasses, were the number one victim.

A crow feeds on a road-killed squirrel in Northampton

Part of the explanation for why squirrels so frequently expire on highways is the sheer number of squirrels. However, part of the explanation may also be the strange mind of the squirrel. It may go half way across a road, see a car, and dart back right under the wheels.

Among road-killed mammals in the survey (which did not include domestic cats and dogs), the numbers went like this: 1,488 gray squirrels, 445 opossums, 270 raccoons (before the current raccoon rabies outbreak that began in New York in 1990), 196 striped skunks, 194 cottontail rabbits, 111 woodchucks, 100 chipmunks, 77 muskrats and 56 red squirrels.

Although residents of the air, birds nearly always end their lives on the ground, many of them on the highways of America. (A few are plucked from midair by predatory birds.) The survey included 1,000 road-killed birds, and it found 166 pigeons, 163 robins (they tend to fly low across the road), 80 starlings, 75 blue jays, 65 gray catbirds (another low flyer), 62 grackles, 41 flickers (a fatal attraction to ants), 33 eastern screech owls (they chase flying insects), 32 crows (they scavenge roadkill) and 31 mourning doves.

Why aren't chipping and house sparrows, ever-present on road shoulders, high on the list? Perhaps it is just good instincts and maneuverability.

Then there is the question of what becomes of roadkill. In many communities, highway crews remove the remains. But often, nature supplies its own cleanup crew, from microscopic bacteria to scavengers as large as turkey vultures. Crows, raccoons, coyotes and even an occasional red-tailed hawk also feed in traffic.

Turkey vultures

The undertakers of the air, turkey vultures may spend most of the day soaring in the sky, searching for food using both their eyesight and keen sense of smell. The odor they are seeking is ethyl mercaptan, a chemical created by rotting meat.

However, circling vultures do not necessarily mean there is a dead animal below. The birds could just be traveling higher on a thermal, a rising column of warm air. Riding these thermals, a turkey vulture with a wingspan of about six feet can glide for as much as six hours without once beating its wings.

Turkey vultures feed on dead animals. They will not circle or stalk a dying or healthy animal. However, plant matter is also a part of their diet.

The males and females are identical in appearance. Both have a bald red head (like a turkey).

The reason it is bald is that when a turkey vulture is feeding, it may have to stick its head into the carcass to find meat, and if there were feathers on its head, they would catch bits of the animal, including any parasites or bacteria it might harbor.

Black bear

Garter snakes may have 40 of them, opossums usually have about eight, catbirds often have four, and bats and porcupines have just one.

What are they? They're offspring. And different species of animals may have very different numbers of young when they become parents.

There are other differences as well in the reproductive habits of animals. Birds, butterflies and frogs lay eggs, but mammals, such as foxes, chipmunks and bears, have live young. Turtles may never meet their mothers, deer fawns may stay with their mothers nearly a year, and crows may stay together as a family composed of several generations.

But like most things that animals do, there is a purpose and a plan to the way they raise their families.

Frequently in their development, species face choices. To best ensure that a species survives, does it have a lot of young or just a few? Does it spend a lot of time taking care of the offspring or very little?

For instance, if a mother has lots of young each season, the chances are greater that some will survive to adulthood so they too can have families and keep the species alive. However, if she does have lots of young, she will have a harder time feeding them than if she has just a few babies. So which approach is best for species survival?

Animals do not consciously choose to use one approach or another. Essentially, life makes the decision for them. Let's say there is a species of animal in which litter size varies greatly. Some mothers have the biological trait – the genes – for having small litters, and some have the genes for large litters. But let's say that because of a permanent change in the availability of food, the young from small litters are more likely to survive. These young would inherit

Deer fawn

Red fox kit

the genes for small litters from their parents, and when they get to be parents, they will have small litters too. In not too many generations, most families of this species may be having small litters, and large litters might disappear completely.

If a species has been around a long time, chances are its method of reproduction has worked well. It is probably right for its situation.

For instance, birds need to be light to fly, and they need to eat a lot of food in comparison to their weight in order to have the energy to fly. They might have had a hard time surviving if they did not lay eggs. A mother bird might weigh too much to fly and feed if she were carrying her young inside her as they developed. She might also be more vulnerable to predators. So eggs that develop and hatch outside a mother's body are a good solution for birds.

Sometimes different approaches to reproduction work just as well. Some snakes, such as garter snakes, have live young, while others, such as milk snakes, lay eggs. The fact that snakes using each method are common seems to indicate neither method has a clear advantage for snakes.

Spring is the time for most offspring. Baby red foxes, woodchucks and river otters might be born just as spring starts. Mallards often lay eggs in April that hatch in May. Bobcats, skunks and chipmunks might have their young in May. Most songbirds, such as northern cardinals and tree sparrows, lay their eggs in May and June. Deer and little brown bats might be born in June.

For animals that are cared for by their parents, how long they remain in the nest or den varies by species. But as a general rule, the larger an animal is, the longer it will stay in the care of its parents.

An American goldfinch feeding its young

Bobcat kitten

The birds and the bees: Family planning in the animal kingdom

PAINTED TURTLE – From three to 14 eggs are laid in a hole dug on land in late spring, then the mother leaves the nest permanently. The eggs take about 75 days to hatch, then the young find water on their own.

GREEN FROG – As many as 4,000 eggs are laid in jelly-like masses in water, typically in mid-spring. The eggs hatch in three to six days, and the young may spend a year as tadpoles before changing into frogs.

HONEY BEE – The queen bee may lay up to 2,000 eggs a day and 200,000 eggs a season. An egg develops in a wax cell in the hive's brood area, hatching in about three days.

RED-TAILED HAWK – Typically, two or three eggs are laid in a stick nest built high in a tall tree. The eggs hatch in about a month. The young take first flights about 45 days later.

MEADOW VOLE – Also called field mice, these small mammals may have as many as 10 litters of live young a year, and there may be up to nine young per litter. The young may spend only two weeks being fed by their mother before they are on their own.

GARDEN SPIDER – Hundreds of eggs are laid in a sac on a leaf, twig or a support in the fall. The mother dies when the weather turns cold and the spiderlings overwinter in the egg sac.

WHITE-TAILED DEER – Usually two fawns are born in late May or early June. They feed on their mother's milk for about three weeks, then they begin to browse on vegetation. Males may leave their mothers by the fall. Females may stay with them up to two years.

RACCOON – Typically, three to seven young are born in a hollow tree in April or May. The young, which have the characteristic mask of raccoons soon after birth, venture from the den in about seven weeks to run and climb.

PUMPKINSEED – Using his fins, the male carves out a saucer-shaped nest in sand or gravel in shallow water in May or June. The female lays 1,700 or more eggs that hatch in as little as three days.

GARTER SNAKE – Females give birth to live young. The litter, delivered between July and September, may number 14 to 40 young. The newborns are immediately on their own.

Baby skunk

Magnolia warblers in their nest

What do you do if you find a baby animal?

You're walking through a field and come across a baby fawn standing motionless and alone in the tall grass. You find a baby bird beneath a tree in your back yard and there's no sign of either parent nearby. You accidentally uncover a nest of baby rabbits in thick grass on the edge of a lawn. What do you do?

Wildlife officials like to say, "If you care, leave them there."

In the majority of cases, an animal that appears to be orphaned really isn't. The mother may have wandered off in search of food, or she may be close by, waiting for you to leave. However, it may be that a young animal is out on its own. In the first days that animals leave the nest or den, they learn valuable lessons about finding food and protecting themselves that they will never have the chance to learn if you take them in without a good reason.

If the baby animal is truly abandoned or if you see an ani-mal, baby or adult, that is obviously injured, call a veteri-narian, an animal control officer or a licensed wildlife reha-bilitator. If it's in your back yard, keep pet cats and dogs away while you wait.

If you decide it is necessary and safe to handle the ani-mal, wear thick gloves and put it in a box with air holes and material, such as leaves or grass, on the bottom so that the animal does not slide around. Handle it as little as possible and call a wildlife officer.

However, it's not true that a mother animal will reject a baby if it has been touched by a human. She will take it back.

Most important, if the animal seems agitated or aggres-sive, do not handle it. Mammals, such as raccoons, foxes, skunks and bats, can carry rabies, a dangerous disease that can be passed to humans through an infected ani-mal's saliva.

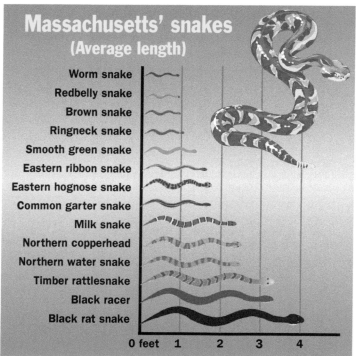

Milk snake

Snakes can awaken primitive fears in us. The sudden discovery of a snake sunning itself on the front walk or slithering through the garden is enough to startle almost anyone.

But despite the impressive size of some native snakes of Massachusetts (the black rat snake can reach a length of up to eight feet), the chance of encountering one that could truly do you harm is very small. Of the 14 species of snakes that are native to the state, only two are venomous – the timber rattlesnake and the northern copperhead.

They were both hunted with such intensity over the centuries that perhaps fewer than a thousand of each still exist in Massachusetts. They are now found only in a few remote spots in the state, places humans rarely inhabit, such as locations high on rocky mountainsides.

Snakes live everywhere in Massachusetts, from the Berkshires to Nantucket. You're most likely to see a snake in the spring, when it is out of hibernation and basking in the sun.

The snake you're most likely to see is the garter snake, the most common snake in the state. Many snakes, such as the black racer, lay eggs, but others, such as the garter snake, have live young.

The northern water snake is the next most common snake in the state. A harmless snake, it is frequently mis-

Northern copperhead

Ringneck snake

taken for the poisonous water moccasin, also called the cottonmouth. However, there are no water moccasins north of Virginia.

The damage from being bitten by a non-venomous snake is more psychological than physical. The wound is typically no more serious than being scratched by a thorn of a rosebush.

Massachusetts' most abundant venomous snake, the northern copperhead prefers rocky landscapes in remote regions.

The timber rattlesnake is the larger of the two venomous snakes

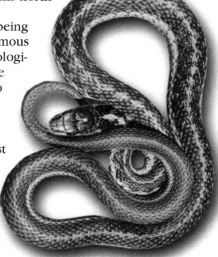

Garter snake

native to the state, typically reaching three to four feet in length. It hunts mainly at night and is most active on nights with a full moon when it will wait in ambush for prey like chipmunks, squirrels or rabbits. It will then lunge at the animal, dig in its fangs, inject its venom, then

Massachusetts' snakes
(Average length)

Worm snake
Redbelly snake
Brown snake
Ringneck snake
Smooth green snake
Eastern ribbon snake
Eastern hognose snake
Common garter snake
Milk snake
Northern copperhead
Northern water snake
Timber rattlesnake
Black racer
Black rat snake

0 feet   1   2   3   4

Smooth green snake

Black rat snake

withdraw to wait for the animal to die, which usually takes just a few minutes. If the animal is able to wander off, the rattlesnake will track it down by scent. It will then try to swallow the dead animal whole. Copperheads and timber rattlesnakes may eat only a dozen meals a year.

Smaller snakes usually search for insects, slugs, earthworms or frogs for their meals. Larger snakes may also hunt small rodents and birds.

All snakes swallow their prey whole, usually seizing the animal first with their jaws. Their upper and lower jaws are not connected, allowing some snakes to open their mouth wide enough to swallow prey larger than their head. However, a few snakes, including the black rat snake and milk snake, may firsy wrap their body around the prey and squeeze it to make the kill.

Some snakes, such as the milk snake and black racer, will vibrate their tails as a display to scare away predators. People often mistake this for the rattle of a timber rattlesnake. But the rattlesnake has a very distinct rattle on it that when shaken sounds almost like a baby's rattle.

In winter, snakes in the Northeast hibernate in burrows or hollows or even in holes in the foundations of homes.

Most snakes are hatched or born in the summer, and they are left on their own to find food from the start. As snakes grow, they periodically shed their outer skin – like throwing away an old set of clothes – because they outgrow it. This is called shedding or molting.

"Fatull axadint" on Springfield Mountain

It is perhaps the only death due to a snake bite – and certainly the only one in Massachusetts – that has been immortalized in an American folk song, one that is now more than two centuries old.

"The Pesky Sarpent" (or alternately "On Springfield Mountain"), recorded by the likes of Burl Ives and Woody Guthrie, tells the sad tale of the demise in 1761 of Timothy Merrick (or Myrick) who lived in Wilbraham and is buried in Adams Cemetery there.

According to the song, "The seventh of August sixty one this fatull axadint was done."

Merrick was supposedly bitten while mowing a mead-

Timber rattlesnake

ow on the mountain. In fact, he may have been the last resident of the state to die of a bite from a wild native snake. According to some versions of the folk song, Merrick's intended bride also died when she attempted to suck the poison out of his wound. ("Now Molly had two ruby lips with which the pizen she did sip.")

Each year in the United States on average, 8,000 people are bitten by one of the nation's 20 native venomous snake species. However, only about a dozen of them die. Doctors who treat the victims say most of the incidents involve a copperhead.

Box turtle, 4 to 8.5 in.

Snapping turtle, 8 to 19 in.

Nature does not fix what isn't broken. Despite being slower and more awkward than almost any other animal its size or larger, turtles have changed remarkably little since they first appeared nearly 220 million years ago, well before most dinosaurs. Their basic design – a soft body contained inside a hard shell – has worked very well for them, providing them excellent protection against predators. In fact, some turtles may live 100 years or more.

The chief threat to turtles is humans. Many turtles are disappearing from the wild because they are collected for the pet trade. Some species are vanishing because their nesting sites, the places where they go to lay eggs, have been developed for businesses and homes.

Like snakes, turtles are reptiles, which means they cannot warm their bodies from the inside the way humans and other mammals do. Instead, reptiles must take action to warm up. For instance, they can bask in the sun. On cool spring days or on summer mornings, you will often see turtles in ponds doing just this, as they sit on top of logs or rocks.

Turtles have no teeth. They use their hard bills to scissor apart their food. In water, they eat aquatic insects, fish, frogs and plants. On land, earthworms, snails, grasshoppers, fruits and berries are all part of their diet.

A turtle's shell is both its mobile home and its protection. The top part of the shell, called the carapace, is attached to the turtle's backbone. The lower half of the shell is called the plastron. Despite what you see in cartoons, turtles cannot leave their shells. The box turtle has a hinge on its plastron so that when it pulls in its head and legs to escape a predator the shell closes up, leaving almost no flesh visible.

Turtles have lungs but no gills. Some are able to breathe underwater by absorbing oxygen from the water through their exposed skin. In winter, many turtles settle down into the mud at the bottom of ponds or rivers to hibernate. Land turtles, such as the box turtle, dig beneath soft dirt or decaying leaves to hibernate.

Worldwide, there are nearly 320 species of turtles. Fifteen species can be found in Massachusetts, including five sea turtles. The most common turtle found in the state is the painted turtle. It lives almost anywhere there are bodies of fresh water.

Snapping turtles, which spend most of their time underwater, are the largest inland turtle found in the state, but they are rarely seen except during the breeding season when they come onto land from ponds and lakes to lay eggs. The record weight for the largest snapping turtle found in Massachusetts is 76.5 pounds.

One of the rarest and smallest turtles (about 3.5 inches in length) in North America is the bog turtle. In the Northeast, the largest concentration of bog turtles is believed to be in Berkshire County in three sites managed by conservation groups.

Turtles all lay eggs in the ground. Even a turtle that spends nearly all its life in water comes onto land to bury up to several dozen eggs in a shallow hole it digs in late spring or early summer. Most turtle eggs hatch from August to October, with a peak in September.

Eastern musk turtle, 3 to 5.5 in.

Spotted turtle, 3.5 to 5 in.

Wood turtle, 5 to 9 in.

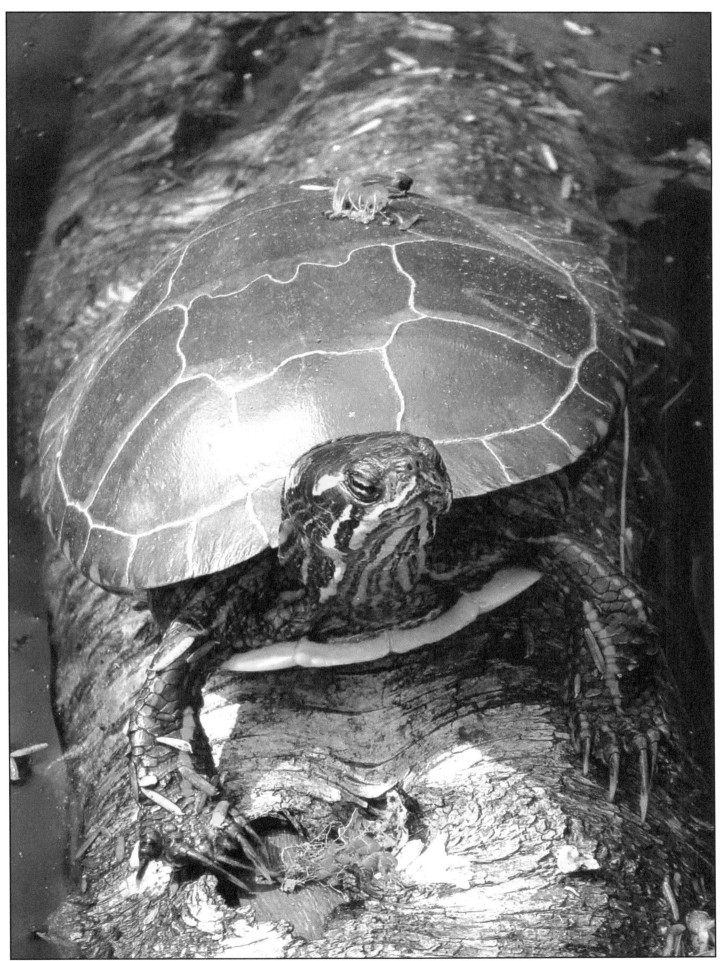

Painted turtle, typically 4 to 10 in., at Arcadia Wildlife Sanctuary in Easthampton

If there were an animal Olympics, frogs would certainly be competitors in the standing long jump. Some can leap more than 30 times their body length.

Lots of animals are specialists physically. They have a feature that gives them an advantage over other animals in finding food or defending themselves, and that's why their species has survived over the centuries. Frogs use their tremendous jumping ability both to escape predators and to pounce on a meal.

Frogs are amphibians, which means they spend part of their lives in water and part on land. They are also among the animals that undergo metamorphosis, which means a "change in form." As young tadpoles (also called polliwogs), they live in water and look like small fish with large rounded heads. They have gills, tails and no legs. But eventually they develop lungs and legs, they will lose their tails and, as frogs, they will be able to live on land.

There may be nearly 4,800 species of frogs worldwide. (This includes toads, which technically are a kind of frog.) Some 10 species of frogs can be found in Massachusetts.

Most adult frogs have large hind legs for jumping, hind toes that are connected by webbing, no claws and tiny teeth (if they have any at all).

Some, such as the eastern spadefoot, are rare enough in the state that you will probably never come across one in your

Bullfrog, 3 to 8 in.

lifetime. But others, like bullfrogs and green frogs, are so common that you can't miss them. In spring or summer, walk down to the edge of any pond and you may see a green frog sitting very still on the bank or a bullfrog peering at you from the water, its two bulging eyes and a bit of its head breaking the pond's surface.

Spend any time around a pond and you'll also hear frogs calling, or chorusing, especially during breeding season, which usually peaks in the spring. Male frogs are the ones making all the noise. They call to attract females and to announce that a territory is theirs. A frog enhances its call by using a loose pouch of skin at its throat that it can fill with air. When it calls, the sound enters this air-filled chamber and reverberates, like an echo in a cave, becoming even more intense. A male frog might repeat its call thousands of times in one night.

Nearly all female frogs lay jellylike eggs in water, often thousands of eggs at a time, which eventually hatch to become tadpoles.

In winter, frogs become inactive, settling down into the mud at the bottom of ponds or taking refuge under piles of dead leaves or in underground tunnels on land. In the coldest weather, some even partially freeze but are still able to thaw out and resume their lives in the spring.

Most frogs eat insects, such as ants and flies, as well as worms and snails. However, the bullfrog, which is the largest

Frog or toad?

You can usually tell the two apart by the texture of their skins. Frogs tend to have smoother skin, and they spend a lot of time in and around water. Toads have rougher, warty skin and usually can be found on land.

Leopard frog, 2 to 5 in.

American toad, 2 to 4.5 in.

Green frog, 2 to 4 in.

native Massachusetts frog, will eat fish, snakes, mice and even small birds or newly hatched turtles that venture too close.

In recent years, biologists have noticed a growing problem among amphibians. Many have deformities, such as missing or extra limbs. In addition, populations of frogs in some places in the world are declining dramatically. Researchers are not sure what the reason is for the troubling problem. A leading theory is that it may be due to a disease or pesticides.

Gray treefrog, 1.5 to 2 in.

Humans vs. animals

The peak performance of humans as of 2015 compared with the observed performance of animals in the wild

Marathon
(26 miles, 385 yards)
Human: 2 hr., 2 min., 57 sec.
Pronghorn antelope: About 45 min.

High jump
Human: 8 ft., .5 in.
Killer whale: 15 to 17 ft.

Speed on land
(100 meter dash)
Human: 9.58 sec.
Cheetah: About 3.2 sec.

Speed in water
(100 meter freestyle)
Human: 46.91 sec.
Sailfish: About 3.3 sec.

Long jump
Human: 29 ft., 4.3 in.
Snow leopard: About 50 ft.

Vernal pools

On the first warm night that follows a heavy rain each spring, an amazing event occurs. Certain frogs and salamanders that are rarely seen at any other time of the year come out of hiding and begin moving through the woods in great numbers.

Crowds of frogs. Parades of salamanders.

They are migrating to pools of water left by melted snow on forest floors. They may cross roads, hike up hills and climb over rocks and fallen trees in their determination to reach these temporary patches of water, called vernal pools.

Because the water dries up in the heat of summer, these pools do not contain fish. That makes them ideal breeding ponds for these amphibians, since there will be no predatory fish in the water to eat their eggs or their developing young.

In Western Massachusetts, wood frogs make this trek, as do spotted, blue-spotted and Jefferson salamanders.

During March and April, you can locate some of these breeding pools by the sounds that come from them at night. Wood frogs will chorus, making a noise that resembles ducks quacking.

Once these amphibians reach their vernal pool, which they may return to year after year, they must court, breed and lay their eggs in a short period of time.

They are active by day, but most of the activity is at night, especially among the salamanders.

If you can locate a vernal pool in the spring, take a flashlight, shine it on the water after dark, and you might see dozens of these creatures swimming about.

Spotted salamander 6 to 10 in.

Wood frog, 1.5 to 3.5 in.

What monarch butterflies do each fall is just about the definition of impossible.

Each September, tens of millions of these regal orange and black butterflies leave their summer breeding grounds in the United States and Canada and flutter off toward their winter home on a few remote mountainsides in Central Mexico. They return to the very same trees that previous generations returned to in their southern migrations for perhaps thousands of years. Then, in March, they may lift off nearly all at once, forming great clouds of butterflies that fill the sky as they return north.

A monarch butterfly rests in a field during migration

But the astounding thing is that adult monarchs may live less than one month in summer. That means that none of the monarchs that leave Mexico in the spring are among those that return in the fall. Instead, it is often their great-great-grandchildren that will somehow find their way back to those few Mexican mountainsides with no one in their band of migrating monarchs ever having been there.

How do they do it? Is it in their genes? Are they guided by the Earth's magnetic field? Or is it just one of the mysteries of animal instincts?

Butterflies, like most insects, go through a metamorphosis, or a change in appearance, except that for butterflies it is one of the most striking changes.

Butterflies have four stages to their lives – egg, larva (also called a caterpillar), pupa (also called a chrysalis), then adult butterfly.

In the pupa stage, the caterpillar forms a shell-like covering around itself and hangs by thin threads from

a twig or leaf. Inside, the caterpillar can change from a fairly clumsy, slow-moving and perhaps, to some, even ugly creature into what can be a beautiful, brilliantly colored butterfly, carrying the colors of a rainbow on its fragile wings.

Butterflies feed on nectar, a sweet liquid produced deep inside flowers. To do this, a butterfly uses its proboscis, a long narrow tube like a drinking straw that can be almost as long as its body. When it's not in use, the proboscis is kept curled up where you would expect the butterfly's mouth to be.

Butterflies need the heat of the sun to warm their bodies, so they tend to be most active during the middle of the day. At night, they rest.

Butterflies have three body parts – the head, the thorax or middle section, and the abdomen. They have six legs, and four wings – a pair each of front and back wings.

The colors on their wings are created by tiny colored scales that fit together like tiles in a mosaic.

Most adult butterflies live only two to four weeks, surviving long enough to mate and produce eggs. The female searches for certain kinds of plants on which to lay her eggs, since they are food plants for the young caterpillars. Monarchs choose milkweed. White admirals like wild cherry and poplar leaves. Tiger swallowtails prefer black cherry leaves.

There are about 100 species of butterflies that breed in Massachusetts. There are nearly 30 other species that are occasionally seen in the state, sometimes carried here by a large storm or on strong winds from other states or regions of the country.

Butterfly or moth?

There are lots of differences. Butterflies usually fly during the day. Moths usually fly at night.

Butterflies tend to rest with their wings folded up over their heads or stretched flat to each side. Moths often lay their wings flat and behind them while resting.

The antennae of butterflies are thin and end in a knob. Those of moths do not end in a knob and are often feathery. Butterflies usually have bolder and brighter colors than moths, although there are some strikingly colored moths.

Baltimore checkerspot

Eastern black swallowtail

The science of butterfly wings

Butterflies are the super-models of the insect king-dom, garbed in spectacular colors and sensational designs.

However, all that artistry has more purpose than to please the human eye. The hues, patterns and other fea-tures carried on those fragile wings have multiple purpos-es, all of them critical to sur-vival – discouraging preda-tors, generating heat and wooing the opposite sex.

For instance, some butter-flies have evolved to have a feature on their wings called eyespots, which help to dis-courage predators. The little wood satyr has a pair of eye-spots on the edges of both its front and back wings. They are spots that may appear to a poor-sighted pred-ator to look like eyes. They can startle a predator like a bird or snake, buying the but-terfly an instant of time in which to make its escape.

Swallowtail butterflies have small projections at the ends of their wings that look like tails (thus their name). These features evolved to attract the attention of predators who may attack the false tails, which tear off easily, giving the butterfly a chance to escape.

Butterflies, like snakes, frogs and turtles, don't have a way to create heat inside their body, the way humans do. They are the temperature of their surroundings and often have to warm up by basking in the sun.

People know that if they wear dark colors on a sunny day, they are likely to be warmer than if they wear light colors. Dark colors, such as brown and black, absorb more sunlight than light col-ors, such as yellow or white, and the absorbed sunlight creates heat.

The tail of the eastern tiger swallowtail, which tears away easily, can be a misleading target for predators.

The dark coloring of a mourning cloak absorbs sunlight, which creates heat in cold weather.

The eyespots of a little wood satyr may fool predators into attacking the outer wing edges instead of the head.

For butterflies, which need a way to generate heat on a cool day, this trait is important. Nearest to their bodies, most butterflies have dark colors. That's because butterflies need a body temperature of at least 80 degrees to fly well. Their muscles won't work prop-erly otherwise. For this reason, butterflies that fly in the early spring or late fall or that over-winter as adults in the state, such as mourning cloaks, tend to have darker coloring.

However, the need for dark colors farther out on the wings isn't as great as it is near the body. That's because very little blood circulates in the wings and they are only able to trans-fer heat for a short distance.

Reproduction does require bright colors and distinctive patterns somewhere on a but-terfly, not only to attract the eye of the opposite sex, but also to identify it as being of the same species. Females choose males based on how nicely and brightly colored they are. Males make the same kind of choices.

Once you know all this, an eastern tiger swallowtail's fea-tures makes a lot more sense: dark near its body for heat, false tails on its wings to foil predators, and fantastic yellow coloring with black patterns on most of its wings to lure a mate.

The design of butterflies, besides being functional, is quite ancient. Human beings have only been around about two million years, but physical-ly and intellectually we are a species that has changed dra-matically. Butterflies, on the other hand, have been flitting from flower to flower and sport-ing colorful patterns on their wings for more than 40 million years, with few evolutionary alterations. That must mean their design has worked well for them.

CHECKLIST
Common butterflies

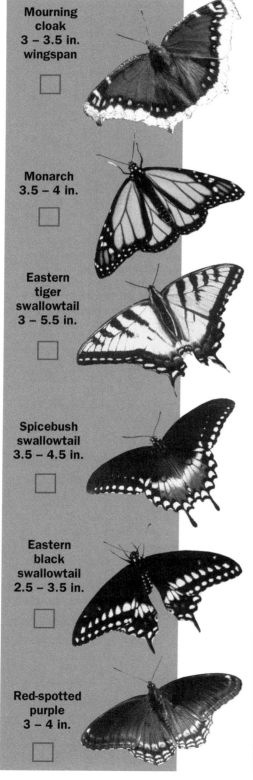

Mourning cloak
3 – 3.5 in. wingspan
☐

Monarch
3.5 – 4 in.
☐

Eastern tiger swallowtail
3 – 5.5 in.
☐

Spicebush swallowtail
3.5 – 4.5 in.
☐

Eastern black swallowtail
2.5 – 3.5 in.
☐

Red-spotted purple
3 – 4 in.
☐

Red admiral
2 – 2.5 in.
☐

Great spangled fritillary
2 – 3 in.
☐

Baltimore checkerspot
1.5 – 2.5 in.
☐

Pearl crescent
1 – 1.5 in.
☐

Eastern comma
1.5 – 2 in.
☐

American copper
About 1 in.
☐

Painted lady
2 – 2.5 in.
☐

Spring azure
About 1 in.
☐

Cabbage white
1.5 – 2 in.
☐

Clouded sulphur
1.5 – 2 in.
☐

Silver-spotted skipper
1.5 – 2.5 in.
☐

Common ringlet
1 – 2 in.
☐

Little wood satyr
1.5 – 2 in.
☐

Banded hairstreak
1 – 1.5 in.
☐

Approximate flight times for Western Massachusetts butterflies

(▩ = first generation, ▩ = second generation, ▩ = third generation)

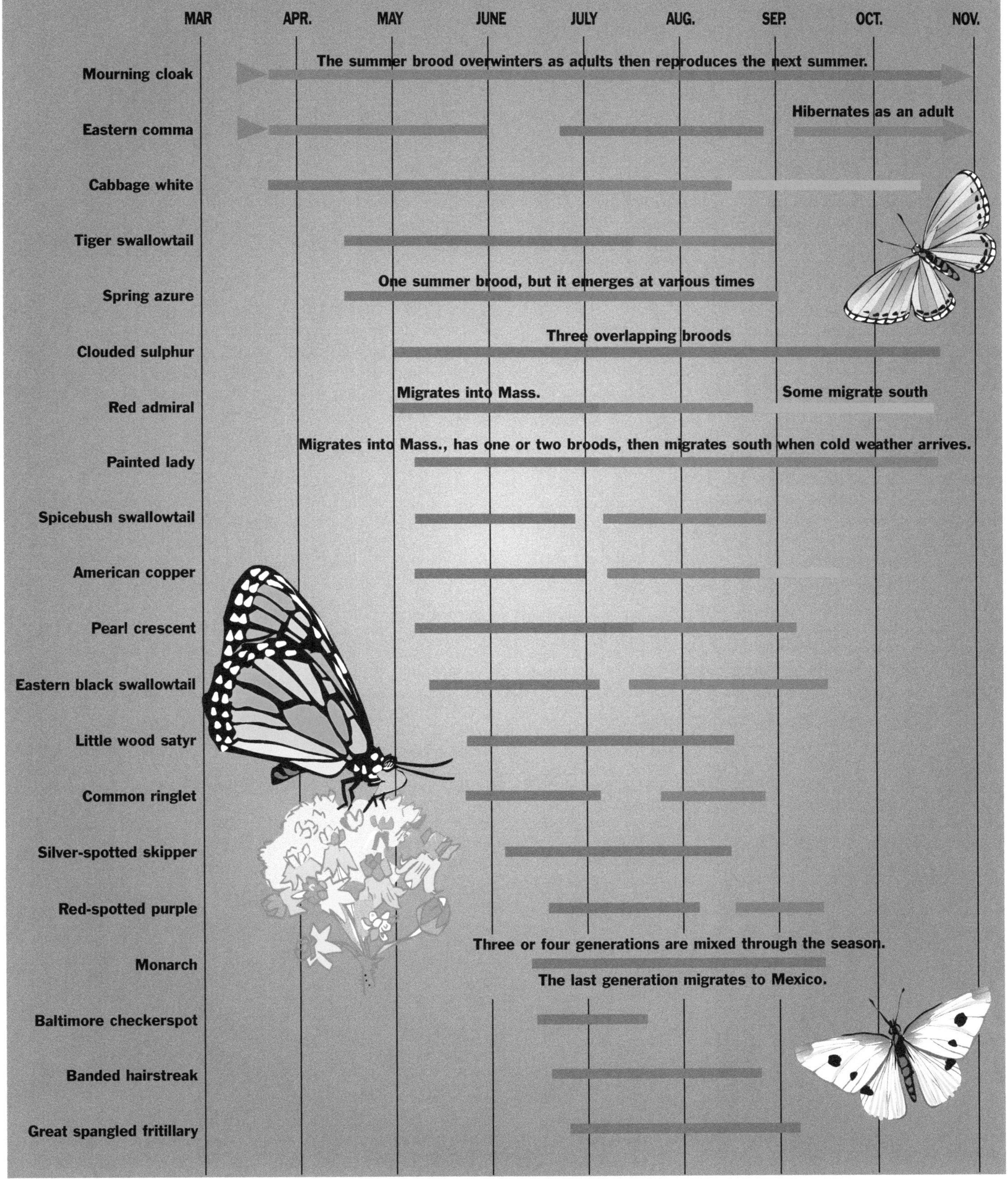

	MAR	APR.	MAY	JUNE	JULY	AUG.	SEP.	OCT.	NOV.

Mourning cloak — The summer brood overwinters as adults then reproduces the next summer.

Eastern comma — Hibernates as an adult

Cabbage white

Tiger swallowtail

Spring azure — One summer brood, but it emerges at various times

Clouded sulphur — Three overlapping broods

Red admiral — Migrates into Mass. / Some migrate south

Painted lady — Migrates into Mass., has one or two broods, then migrates south when cold weather arrives.

Spicebush swallowtail

American copper

Pearl crescent

Eastern black swallowtail

Little wood satyr

Common ringlet

Silver-spotted skipper

Red-spotted purple

Monarch — Three or four generations are mixed through the season. The last generation migrates to Mexico.

Baltimore checkerspot

Banded hairstreak

Great spangled fritillary

At most family reunions, get all the relatives together in one room and you can usually see a resemblance.

But put a caterpillar and a butterfly side by side, or a tadpole and a frog next to each other, and not only is there no family resemblance, there's not even a species resemblance. Why does this happen?

This dramatic change in appearance, this metamorphosis, evolved in nature as a way of ensuring that these species would survive.

Many features of plants and animals – the long legs of a great blue heron, the rich color of a rose, the sharp beak of a hawk – evolved or developed because they give a species a better chance for survival. They are features that give it an edge in finding food or in reproducing or in protecting itself from predators.

Metamorphosis is no different. Species that change form (and all amphibians and nearly all insects go through some type of metamorphosis) can occupy two very different places in the ecosystem. The young may eat one kind of food, go through metamorphosis, and then eat a different kind of food as adults. That means there is more food available for the entire species, increasing its chance for survival.

Tadpoles are vegetarians, but adult bullfrogs eat almost anything, from plants to flying insects. Most caterpillars feed on leaves, but adult butterflies sip the rich nectar they find in flowers.

Having different forms at different stages of life can help in other ways as well. Caterpillars do almost nothing but eat and grow, and they are well-designed to do just that. They are able to avoid predators to some extent because most can blend into vegetation. They are also able to blend into their environment as pupae, the stage in which they are surrounded by mummylike coverings and

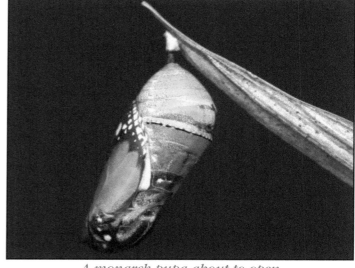
A monarch pupa about to open

Monarch caterpillar

undergo the changes that make them adult butterflies. Then, in the butterfly stage, they can fly to new areas to lay eggs and spread their species.

The changes tadpoles and caterpillars go through during metamorphosis are striking. Bullfrog tadpoles, which will be going from a life spent entirely in water to a life on land and in water, have to develop limbs and lungs during the change, and their tails have to be reabsorbed into their bodies.

Caterpillars, during the pupa stage, have to lose their many legs as well as develop wings and sex organs. They will also develop new mouth parts to draw nectar from flowers as adult butterflies.

For frogs, the metamorphosis usually lasts from several days to a few weeks. For butterflies, it may last from a few days to several months.

Monarch metamorphosis

In about 10 days, the adult butterfly emerges from the pupa, unfolds its wings, which slowly harden, then it flies away.

In the pupa stage, wings develop and the mouth parts change from chewing parts to sucking parts so that the adult butterfly can sip flower nectar.

The caterpillar attaches itself by a silk thread and tiny hooks on its abdomen to a plant stalk and then sheds its skin one last time to reveal the pupa beneath.

Eggs are laid by female monarchs on the undersides of the leaves of milkweed plants. Each larva, or caterpillar, will eat its way out of its egg within a week and then begin to feed on the milkweed.

For the next two to three weeks, the caterpillar will feed and grow, shedding its skin every so often, a process called molting.

Bullfrog metamorphosis

Within an egg, the embryonic cell divides within the first half day, and at four days, the developing tadpole has a tail bud and some muscle movement.

During reproduction, the male clasps the female, and she lays thousands of eggs in water. He then fertilizes the eggs with his sperm.

The frog is a mature adult in about three years. Adult bullfrogs typically weigh about one pound.

The egg hatches in water in about six days, and the tadpole clings to plants underwater. Within a day, it will begin to feed on algae.

A bullfrog spends about two years as a tadpole.

When the metamorphosis starts, hind legs begin to appear, and the gill system is gradually replaced by a lung system.

Within two weeks, the metamorphosis is usually complete. With its lungs, a frog can breathe air.

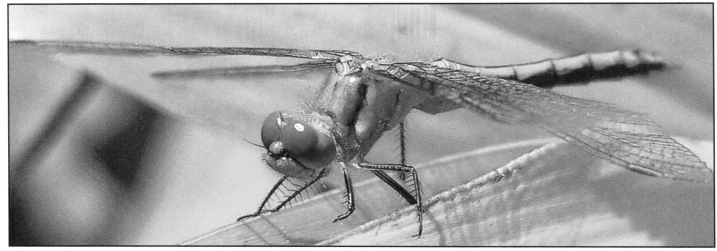

Ruby meadowhawk, female

As if the passion of the public for boldly colored winged creatures can't be satisfied by birds and butter-flies alone, dragonflies are now attracting their faithful followers.

And why not? They are elegant creatures, capable of mid-air acrobatics that few, if any, birds can match. They are also the friends of anyone who doesn't like mosquitoes. The reason dragonflies spend so much time hovering over ponds is that they are hunting mosquitoes, which are their primary food.

Worldwide, there are about 6,000 species in the order Odonata, which includes dragonflies and dam-selflies. Perhaps 165 can be found in Massachusetts – 50 or so species of damselflies and 115 or so of dragonflies.

Like birds, dragonflies fly and lay eggs. Some, like the green darner, even migrate to warmer regions when the weather turns cold. However, like butterflies and other insects, dragonflies undergo metamorphosis, changing from water-bound larvae to flying adults. Unlike butterflies, though, there is no pupa stage.

The eggs of dragonflies, which are laid in or near water, hatch in five to 10 days. The larvae that emerge then begin the process of eating and growing. They consume everything from mosquito larvae to tiny fish, capturing their prey with a unique lower lip that has its own

Twelve-spotted skimmer, male

claw. The lip can shoot out to almost a third of a larva's body length to grab a meal.

Larvae that hatch in the summer often spend the winter growing before transforming into adult dragonflies the following spring.

When it is ready to make the change to a flying adult, the larva climbs out of the water, takes hold of a reed or twig, and sheds its skin, allowing the soft, folded wings beneath to slowly fill with blood and harden. Within an hour or two, the adult dragonfly takes to the air.

Many dragonflies live only about a month as adults, time enough to mate (usually accomplished in mid-air) and to lay eggs before dying.

The flight abilities of dragonflies are indeed impressive. The larger species, such as the darners, may be capable of flying up to 50 miles per hour. Seemingly tireless, they may spend most of the day in the air, catching prey on the wing.

What makes them such powerful aviators? For one thing, like a hummingbird, a high percentage of their body mass is dedicated to flight. A sexually mature male may be more than 60 percent flight muscle.

Dragonflies can take off backward, they can launch vertically like a helicopter, and they can hover motionless for more than a minute. They can also stop on a dime.

Dragonfly or damselfly?

Dragonflies and damselflies are both found flying over ponds, swamps and other still water bodies. You can tell the two apart by how they hold their wings when at rest. A dragonfly will stretch them out from side to side. Damselflies, which have thin, needle-like bodies, rest with their wings folded in back of them close to their sides. Contrary to myth, neither drag-onflies nor dam-selflies bite humans.

Dragonfly   Damselfly

Halloween pennant, male

Dragonflies mating

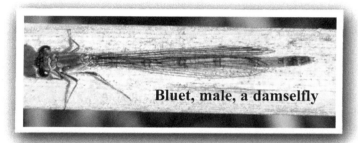

Bluet, male, a damselfly

Green darner, female

American lady

Monarch

Eastern tiger swallowtail

What tangled webs they weave. Worldwide, nearly 44,000 kinds of spiders have been identified, including about 3,000 in the United States and nearly 700 species in New England.

You can tell a spider by its two body sections and eight legs. (Since insects have only six legs, spiders are not true insects.)

Interestingly, most spiders also have eight eyes, with some found on the side instead of the front of their bodies. Yet, spiders have poor eyesight generally.

Many spiders are active only at night, and most are not very aggressive. Even those with the strongest venom will attack humans only as a defensive measure, preferring to retreat from battle whenever possible.

Because of the Northeast's chilly winters, most spiders found in Massachusetts live just one season, hatching in the spring, breeding and laying eggs in the summer, and dying in the fall. But a certain number manage to live through the winter. They may try to escape harsh weather by seeking refuge in the cozy interior of your home or apartment. A large house can be home to hundreds of spiders in winter, with the human residents barely aware of their presence.

Most spiders you are likely to encounter in Massachusetts would be too small to pose a threat. As a general rule, only those with a body over half an inch in length (not including legs) have fangs capable of penetrating human skin. But that does not mean they are dangerous. Even larger spiders that bite are not usually a serious danger.

Just about all spiders are venomous. Even the smaller

The multiple eyes of a spider

ones use venom to weaken or kill their prey. But only a few spiders have strong enough venom to cause harm to a human being.

The two most venomous spiders to be found in the United States are the brown recluse and the black widow. However, most people recover if bitten by either.

Both are occasionally discovered in Western Massachusetts, usually arriving as stowaways on furniture or in clothes brought into the area by people coming from other regions where the spiders are more common.

Among the largest spiders you might cross paths with in Massachusetts are these two, shown their actual size. They can be found in homes or sheds near forested areas. Their venom is not poisonous to humans.

Brownish-gray fishing spider, female, 1 in.   *Wolf spider, female, 1 in.*

Nursery web spider, female, .6 in.

The brown recluse has a violin-shaped mark on its back. Its bite can have serious effects and must be treated quickly.

The female black widow is black with a red marking on her abdomen that is shaped like an hourglass. The female earned her name because soon after mating she may eat the male. The males of most species of spiders are not treated so badly.

Crab spider, female, .4 in.

One of the largest spiders someone in Massachusetts` might encounter indoors is the wolf spider, often a resident of garden sheds and suburban gardens. However, sometimes it is an invader of homes. Its body can be more than an inch long. While painful, its bite usually does not have long-lasting effects. In most species, the female is larger than the male.

Southern black widow spider, female, .5 in.

Brown recluse spider, female, .4 in.

Spider webs

The delicate webs that decorate dew-covered meadows or that float weightlessly in the corners of attic ceilings are actually wonders of engineering. Pound for pound, the silk in a spider web is stronger than steel.

Spiders produce the silk in their abdomens. It starts out as a sticky gel made of pure protein that is created in an array of glands. The gel is pushed down tubes that lead to ducts called spinnerets that will shoot it out of the body.

By contracting its abdomen muscles, a spider is able to push out the gel from thousands of tiny spigots on the spinnerets. In the process, the gel changes to a solid. And like the many fibers that come together to create hemp rope, so the many strands exiting the spigots come together to create the finished silk line.

The final strand of silk may be less than a tenth the thickness of a human hair, but it can hold an astounding amount of weight.

As a comparison, a rope that is an inch thick would have to support as many as 15 automobiles to have the same strength as some spider silk.

Aside from creating webs with their silk to snare passing flies and other prey, spiders use it as a safety line so that they can drop down from ceilings or branches. They also use silk to wrap their eggs for protection and to wrap prey for a later meal. A spider may produce up to eight kinds of silk, each for a different use.

Watch a colony of ants around their nest in a field or a swarm of gnats on a pond in summer and almost inevitably the question occurs to you.

Just how many insects are there in the world?

Well, science has an answer – or at least a rough estimate. At any given moment on the planet, there are about 10 quintillion of them. That's roughly 10,000,000,000,000,000,000 mayflies, millipedes, monarchs, mantises and more.

An impressive number, it's the best guess of famed Harvard entomologist E. O. Wilson. To put it in perspective, 10 quintillion is more than the number of seconds that would have ticked on a clock if it began keeping time the moment the universe began.

Worldwide, nearly a million species of insects have been identified. That's more than the number of all other species of animals combined. (There may be nearly 5,500 species of mammals and about 10,000 species of birds.) However, scientists say they have recorded only a fraction of all the insect species that actually exist, which they say may number more than two million.

Insects are found in just about every environment on Earth, including in Antarctica where several dozen species of insects have been seen.

If for no other reason than their sheer numbers, insects are arguably

Bumblebee, .7 in.

Honey bee, .5 in.

Bee or wasp?

Both can sting if bothered. Bees tend to have hairy bodies while wasps usually do not. Many bees, such as bumblebees and honey bees, have on their hind legs "pollen baskets" made of stiff hairs, where they carry the pollen they collect on their visits to flowers. Wasps do not have them. Hornets and yellow jackets are kinds of wasps.

Bumblebee   **Paper wasp**

the most successful animals on the planet. Sure, they can be some of the most repellent creatures known to humankind, but they are perhaps more necessary to our survival than any other group of animals. They play a critical role in the ecology of Earth in ways that most people don't realize. Should insects all disappear at once, humans would soon follow since the lives of insects and humans are so intertwined.

Why? Insects are eaten by small animals, which are in turn eaten by bigger animals, which might ultimately be eaten by humans, so the entire food chain would fall apart. Also, insects pollinate the majority of fruits and vegetables humans eat, including apples, oranges, blueberries, cranberries, cherries, melons and almonds. Insects also break down dead plants and animals as well as animal wastes into the nutrients that fertilize the soil, allowing things to grow.

Then, there is the less measurable spiritual loss the disappearance of beetles and butterflies, ladybugs and waterbugs, would create. Most flowering plants, including field wildflowers, are pollinated by insects, so they would also disappear. Indeed, some of the poetry would go out of our daily lives.

Insects are the ultimate survivors, despite their small size and short lives. (Some adult mosquitoes are lucky to live two weeks). In fact, their brief lives

Woolly bear caterpillar, 2 in.

Praying mantis, 3.5 in.

True katydid, 2 in.

help make them so suc-
cessful in surviving
change. Insects reproduce
quickly and in great num-
bers. So if there is any
change in their surround-
ings – for instance, if the
temperature warms dra-
matically – the chances
are good that they will
produce some young from
the thousands of eggs they
might lay (some termite
queens produce 30,000
eggs a day) that have the
right combination of
genes to overcome the
warmer weather. Some of
those young will survive,
reproduce more young
with similar genes, and
soon the local population
will have adapted to the
warmer climate and be thriving again.

Pennsylvania leather-wing

moths and beetles smell
with their antennae.
Most insects have two
main eyes and two or
three smaller, simpler
eyes. The main eyes are
sometimes made up of
thousands of individual
lenses, each of which produces an image. Human
eyes have one lens each,
so the human brain has to
interpret only the two
images that its eyes send
it. But a dragonfly's eyes
may have 28,000 lenses
each, which means its
tiny brain has to interpret
that many separate signals
in order to understand
what it is seeing.
Nearly every insect goes
through metamorphosis, a

Species that take a relatively long time to reproduce,
such as some birds, which may have just two or three
young a season, would not be able to adapt to dramatic
changes in their habitat so quickly. Such changes might
completely wipe out their local population.

All insects have certain things in common. They have
six legs, three body sections and antennae. Spiders, with
their eight legs, are not true insects. Most insects can
hear, taste, touch, smell and see, but many of them do
these things in very different ways than humans. Crickets
hear with their knees. Flies taste with their feet. Some

change in appearance marking a new stage of its life. Most
insects look different as adults than as young emerging
from eggs. Many are flightless when young but have wings
as adults.

Big bugs

Here are a few of the larger
insects that can be found in
Western Massachusetts. They
are shown their actual sizes.

*Luna
moth*

*Fiery
searcher*

*Eastern
dobsonfly*

*Dogday harvestfly
(cicada)*

Fireflies

Also called lightning bugs, these beetles produce light in the tips of their abdomens by combining chemicals they produce and store in their bodies. Their blinking in summer is part of their mating process. Males fly about, flashing their lights to attract females that sit on leaves and branches.

There are nearly 200 species of fireflies in North America. A few don't flash, but those that do have their own pattern of flashes to help males and females of the same species identify each other.

In the East, the male of one of the most common fireflies (*Photinus pyralis*) flashes in low flight over grass about every six seconds, creating a yellowish "J" that lasts about half a second as he lifts into the air. The female, which sits on vegetation nearby, responds about two seconds later with a half-second flash of her own, an invitation for him to approach.

Ants

Like bees and other social insects, ants live in organized societies in which the members work together to keep the colony functioning. In all ant colonies, one queen ant is responsible for laying the eggs and producing the young.

Black carpenter ants, which are about a half-inch long, build their nests in dead wood, creating a series of tunnels and rooms. Unlike termites, they do not eat wood. They only tunnel into it.

Little black ants, which may be one-fourth the size of carpenter ants, usually build their nest underground, forming a little mound at the opening.

Mosquitoes

It is only the female mosquito that will bite you. The males feed mainly on flower nectar and fruit juices. The females need a meal of blood before laying eggs. Mosquitoes are most active at dawn, at dusk and at night. They hatch from eggs that develop in water, such as rainwater that collects in roadside ditches or in discarded tires.

Grasshoppers and crickets

The "songs" of grasshoppers, like those of crickets, are the music of summer nights. However, these insects don't sing the way humans do. Grasshoppers rub a rough part of a back leg against their wings to create their music, and crickets rub their wings together. They make these noises to attract females and to chase away other males.

Ladybugs

Probably the best known of beetles, ladybugs are among the most valuable beetles to humans. They generally do not eat plants, but they do eat small insects that eat plants, which makes them important to farmers. In this region, you might see ladybugs with as few as zero spots or with as many as 19.

June bugs

Also called May beetles, June bugs are often seen buzzing around porch lights, or they are heard crashing into windows and screens at night.

Unfortunately for them, they are attracted to electric lights. They are harmless to humans, though. As adults, they feed on the leaves of many common trees.

House flies

Unwelcome guests at a picnic and a noisy distraction when they get inside a home or apartment, house flies live short lives and reproduce quickly. But they do not bite.

Their eggs can hatch in just a day, and the larvae can grow to adulthood in a week. A house fly may be hatched, mature, reproduce and die in the space of just a month, which means several generations of house flies can emerge during one summer.

Honey bees

Honey bees live in ordered communities in which each bee has a job. A honey bee hive may have 50,000 members. There is only one queen bee, and her job is to lay eggs. There may be 1,000 male drones in the hive, and their only job is to mate with the queen, although only one will be successful. The rest of the hive's members are female worker bees, and they can have many jobs during their brief lives. Here is the typical life cycle of one worker bee in summer.

DAY 1–3
The egg is laid and develops within a wax cell.

DAY 4–20
The larva emerges from the egg, feeds, and then develops into an adult worker bee.

DAY 21–23
The worker bee's first job is as a cleaner, readying the brood cells for the next batch of eggs.

DAY 24–27
It becomes a nurse, feeding the older larvae.

DAY 28–34
It continues as a nurse, feeding the younger larvae and the queen.

DAY 35–41
It becomes a food collector, searching outside the hive for pollen, a rich source of protein.

DAY 42–death
It continues as a food collector, searching outside the hive for nectar, a rich source of energy.

At different times, the worker bee may also be a fanner (beating its wings to keep the hive cool), an undertaker (removing the bodies of dead bees from the hive), a soldier (guarding the hive's entrance) or a builder (creating wax to add to the hive walls).

Japanese beetle

Cecropia caterpillars

Periodical cicada

Asian ladybug

Red-legged grasshopper

Green bottle fly

Same planet, different worlds.

That's a good definition of ecosystems, the largely self-contained collections of plants, animals and ecological conditions that cover the landscape like different countries on a map.

A pond with bullfrogs, cattails and dragonflies can be near a forest where you might see hemlocks, wolf spiders and white-tailed deer. And just a stone's throw away can be a field where you might find monarch butterflies, oxeye daisies and meadow voles.

An ecosystem is a collection of living and non-living things, including plants, animals, ponds, streams, rocks and dirt, that all interact as a unit.

An ecosystem is created by a particular combination of water, land features, sunlight and temperature. Wherever you find that set of physical conditions in a region, you're likely to find the same general group of plants and animals.

An ecosystem can include a stream or a pond, or it can include a combination of a stream and a pond. An ecosystem can include a meadow in a valley or a meadow on a mountainside.

An ecosystem can be as small as a single small pool of water left from melted snow on a forest floor in spring, or it can be as large as the whole forest, including the pool of water. Ecosystems are also found in cities. A vacant lot between two buildings may eventually become home to a variety of wildflowers, insects, birds and small mammals.

Ecosystems do not have barriers between them, though. They overlap and share resources. Insects, birds and other animals move between ecosystems.

Food web

In any ecosystem, relationships develop between plants and animals in regard to food, and those relationships are called a food web. In a forest ecosystem where oak trees grow, acorns and other nuts are an important element of the food web. Here is just a part of the food web in such a forest. The arrows indicate what feeds on what.

Red-tailed hawk → Gray squirrel → Acorns ← Tufted titmouse ← Sharp-shinned hawk ← Red oak → Sun's energy

Red fox → Deer mouse — Flying squirrel — Wolf spider — Dead wood / Dead leaves

Barred owl → Short-tailed shrew → Earthworm → Mite

In nature, plants and animals depend on each other for food. Many birds eat insects. Many insects eat the leaves of trees and other plants. Trees and other plants draw nutrition through their roots from dead plants and animals that decay on the ground, and they produce nuts and seeds that birds and other animals eat. This is called a food web.

After a long period of time, a balance or a harmony in the food web in an ecosystem is often reached so that populations of the different species stay within certain limits. For instance, if a predator, such as foxes, grows too plentiful, the prey, such as deer mice, might die off. Without enough food, foxes might decline in number and the mice have a chance to grow more plentiful again, allowing foxes to grow in population once again. It is a continuing cycle.

Ecozones of Western Massachusetts

In an ecozone, the same general physical conditions tend to prevail. Here are some of the characteristics of the region's different ecozones.

1 Taconic Mountains

Northern hardwood forest of maple, beech and birch – Streams have steep grades – Peaks over 3,000 feet in elevation (Mt. Greylock is 3,491 feet)

9 Berkshire Valley

Birch, maple, oak, white pine, hemlock – The underlying limestone and marble make surface water alkaline – Hoosic and Housatonic rivers are the main drainage

8 Lower Berkshire hills

Northern and transition hardwoods – Hills 1,000-1,700 feet in elevation – Abundant lakes and ponds

2 Green Mountains – Berkshire highlands

Northern hardwood and spruce-fir forests – Deerfield and upper Westfield rivers are the main drainage

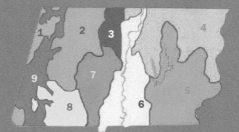

7 Berkshire transition

Maple, oak, white pine, hemlock – Hills 400-1,400 feet in elevation – Westfield and Connecticut rivers are the main drainage

3 Vermont piedmont

Birch, maple, oak, hickory, white pine, hemlock – The underlying limestone makes surface water alkaline – Hills 400-1,400 feet in elevation – Deerfield and Connecticut rivers are the main drainage

4 Worcester – Monadnock plateau

Northern hardwoods but also transition forest of white pine and hemlock – Hills 500-1,400 feet in elevation

5 Lower Worcester plateau – Eastern Connecticut upland

Birch, maple, oak, hemlock and white pine – Hills 500-1,200 feet in elevation – Chicopee and Quinebaug rivers are the main drainage

6 Connecticut River Valley

Central hardwood forest of oak and hickory and transition forest – Connecticut River is the main drainage

Examples of Western Massachusetts ecosystems

Cattail marsh

Often found where soil is semi-permanently flooded and the standing water is shallow, these marshes are dominated by common cattails. The marshes are often beside open water, such as a lake. Red-winged blackbirds may nest among the cattails, and beavers may build lodges nearby. Snapping turtles, water snakes and various frogs, including bullfrogs and green frogs, live here. Skunk cabbage may bloom in the early spring in the shallows or on adjacent land.

Floodplain forest

These are forests found along almost any river or large stream that floods regularly. The tree species found in them typically include silver and black maple, cottonwood, butternut, sycamore, black willow and ash. Plants seen here include jewelweed, Virginia creeper and poison ivy. Birds include red-bellied woodpeckers, cerulean warblers and tufted titmice. Great blue herons may nest in these forests. Amphibians include Jefferson salamanders and leopard frogs.

Rock outcrop

These are areas typically on upper mountain slopes where bedrock is visible and there are only pockets of thin soil. As a result, trees tend to be stunted and other plants can be sparse. Peregrine falcons may nest here and timber rattlesnakes may den here. Mosses and lichens may cover the rocks, but the wildlife found here will depend on the kind of bedrock and its elevation.

Successional old field

When farm land or cleared fields are allowed to grow free, grasses and wildflowers are typically the first plants to take root, followed by smaller shrubs and trees and then finally larger trees that may shade out and eliminate the original undergrowth. Wildflowers found here include New England asters, dandelions and Queen Anne's lace. Animals seen here include eastern cottontails, meadow voles, field sparrows, red foxes, woodchucks and white-tailed deer. Successional old fields occur statewide.

Urban vacant lot

Vacant lots in towns and cities can become home to a range of wildlife. Trees found here include tree-of-heaven, white mulberry and Norway maples. Wildflowers found here include Queen Anne's lace, dock and goldenrod. Birds found here include starlings, house sparrows and pigeons. Mice and chipmunks may also be seen here, and cats may prowl at night, looking for a meal.

Water lily aquatic wetland

Found throughout the state, these ecosystems are often associated with ponds, lakes and slow-moving sections of rivers. Plant species seen here include fragrant water lily and spatterdock. Green frogs, bullfrogs and dragonflies are common, and birds seen here may include great blue herons and mallards.

Northern hardwood forest

The top of these forests – the canopy – is typically closed by leaves, providing shade beneath. Trees found here include sugar maples, yellow birches and American beeches. Mammals found here include white-tailed deer, black bears, porcupines, eastern chipmunks and red squirrels. Birds found here include black-capped chickadees and blue jays. Because of the shading by trees, many wildflowers, such as wood anemones, bloom in the early spring before leaves appear.

Confined river

This is the portion of a stream or river where pools, riffles and flat-water runs occur and where there might be waterfalls and springs. The water is usually fast-flowing and clear. Fish found here include creek chub, common shiners, darters and minnows. Rainbow trout, brown trout and smallmouth bass may have been introduced. Plants found here include waterweed and pondweed.

Appalachian oak forest

This is a forest mainly of hardwood trees that is usually found on ridgetops and slopes. Trees found here include red and white oaks, red maples and hickories. Oaks produce acorns, so animals seen here include those that feed on acorns, such as gray squirrels, deer mice and wild turkeys. Birds seen here include hawks that feed on small mammals, as well as blue jays and tufted titmice. Timber rattlesnakes may also be found here.

A brown trout, bottom, and a northern pike

Bluegill – 4 to 12 in., typical length for adults – fresh water

White perch – 8 to 10 in. – fresh and salt water

Smallmouth bass – 8 to 15 in. – fresh water

Rainbow trout – 10 to 25 in. – fresh and salt water

Striped bass – 18 to 45 in. – fresh and salt water

This planet was made for fish. Nearly 71 percent of the Earth's surface is covered by the oceans. Add in the countless lakes, ponds, rivers and streams on land and it's clear that uncounted billions of fish call all this water home.

Massachusetts has 4,230 miles of rivers flowing through it. The state also has more than 3,000 lakes and ponds. And some 98 species of freshwater fish can be found in these inland waters.

Some fish, such as the yellow perch and bluegill, are found only in freshwater habitats. However, American shad spend most of their time out at sea in salt water, then they come up rivers, including the Connecticut River to spawn (reproduce) in the spring in freshwater environments.

Fish evolved well before land animals, first appearing nearly 500 million years ago. Most scientists believe land animals can claim fish as their ancestors. They believe amphibians, such as salamanders and frogs, evolved directly from fish; reptiles, such as snakes and turtles, evolved from amphibians; and birds and mammals, including human beings, evolved separately from reptiles.

Fish breathe underwater by drawing oxygen from water as it passes over their gills. Sharks are fish, but whales (including dolphins and porpoises, which are kinds of whales) are mammals and they breathe air into their lungs like human beings, holding their breath when they submerge. Some whales can stay submerged for more than an hour on one breath.

Most fish are among those animals whose reproductive strategy is to lay lots of eggs and then abandon them. Enough eggs usually develop that their species will survive. Fish usually produce thousands or even millions of eggs each season.

Many of the state's inland ponds and lakes are very isolated and have never been stocked. Yet, fish somehow manage to find their way into these waters.

Trophy fish

Here are the record weights, in pounds and ounces, as of 2015 for some species of freshwater fish caught in Massachusetts.

Pumpkinseed – 2 lbs., 1 oz.
Yellow perch – 2 lbs., 12 oz.
Crappie – 4 lbs., 10 oz.
Bullhead – 6 lbs., 4 oz.
Brook trout – 10 lbs., 0 oz.
Smallmouth bass – 8 lbs., 2 oz.
Chain pickerel – 9 lbs., 5 oz.
Landlocked salmon –
   10 lbs., 2 oz.
American shad – 11 lbs., 4 oz.
Rainbow trout – 13 lbs., 13 oz.
Largemouth bass – 15 lbs., 8 oz.
Brown trout – 19 lbs., 10 oz.
Lake trout – 24 lbs.
Channel catfish – 26 lbs., 8 oz.
Tiger muskellunge – 27 lbs.
Northern pike – 35 lbs.
Carp – 46 lbs., 4 oz.

How does it happen? Of course, many ponds are connected to others by streams, but some are cut off entirely from other ponds and lakes with fish. Wildlife biologists believe birds may have carried fish eggs in their feathers or on their feet or even in their droppings from one pond to another. Also, violent storms, floods and even tornadoes may have moved fish or their eggs from one pond to another. Such things only have to happen once in a thousand years for a fish population to get started in a pond or lake.

Fishing was the first real industry for European settlers arriving in Massachusetts. The coastal waters were rich in finfish and shellfish, from striped bass and haddock to lobsters and clams. Whaling was also an early industry.

And during the American Revolution, shad caught in the Connecticut River during the spring spawning run became a primary food to help sustain soldiers in the Continental Army throughout the war.

In weather not fit for man or beast, the beasts and other forms of wildlife manage to do a pretty good job of surviving in winter.

Through the ages, plants and animals have gained a variety of tricks for getting through even the most severe winter weather.

Some animals hibernate, sleeping through the worst of it. Others know how and where to avoid biting winds and freezing temperatures and where to find food in a pinch.

Birds can seem the most vulnerable of animals in winter, but they often ride out storms perched high up inside the layered branches of dense evergreen trees, sheltered from the snow and wind, sleeping or eating insects they find in the bark and under limbs. Their feathers offer natural protection from the cold. They can also fluff up their feathers with air for even greater insulation.

In winter, some birds will form great flocks, sometimes thousands of birds, and spend the night together in trees or other suitable locations, partially for warmth and partially for protection from predators and cold winter winds.

In Western Massachusetts, streams of crows can be seen around dusk each day, flying toward their overnight site, called a roost, usally in or around Springfield.

Woodchucks and bats hibernate through the winter.

Raccoon

Red fox

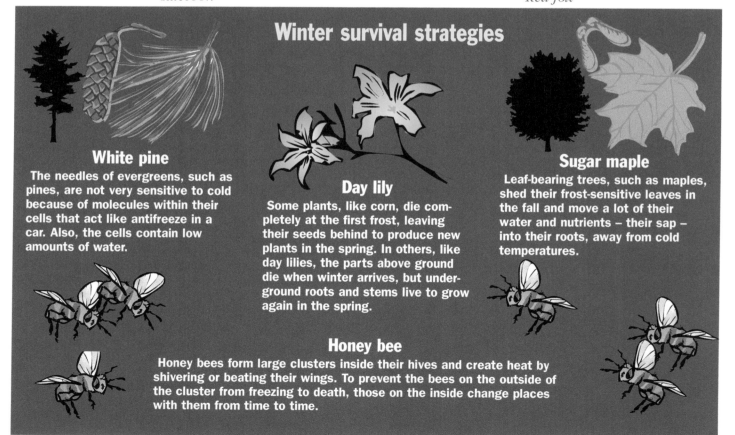

Winter survival strategies

White pine
The needles of evergreens, such as pines, are not very sensitive to cold because of molecules within their cells that act like antifreeze in a car. Also, the cells contain low amounts of water.

Day lily
Some plants, like corn, die completely at the first frost, leaving their seeds behind to produce new plants in the spring. In others, like day lilies, the parts above ground die when winter arrives, but underground roots and stems live to grow again in the spring.

Sugar maple
Leaf-bearing trees, such as maples, shed their frost-sensitive leaves in the fall and move a lot of their water and nutrients – their sap – into their roots, away from cold temperatures.

Honey bee
Honey bees form large clusters inside their hives and create heat by shivering or beating their wings. To prevent the bees on the outside of the cluster from freezing to death, those on the inside change places with them from time to time.

Beavers spent the winter awake in their lodges. Rabbits take refuge in tunnels under snow-covered shrubs or in abandoned woodchuck holes. For these and other mammals, their fur is their winter coat.

For coyotes, red foxes, bobcats and a variety of birds of prey that choose not to migrate, such as red-tailed hawks, winter in this region is business as usual as they prowl and patrol the countryside for a meal. Snow can actually benefit them since it can make prey stand out.

For both plants and animals, the greatest danger of severe cold is that it can freeze water. When water does freeze, it expands and forms sharp-edged ice crystals. The cells of all living things are filled with water, and if that water turns to ice, it can puncture the cell walls, causing damage or even death.

Perhaps the most fantastic trick for surviving freezing

Snowy owl

temperatures is the one used by some frogs. Many frogs spend the winter on land, buried beneath leaves on the forest floor. But it may become so cold that even these places have freezing temperatures. To cope with such conditions, treefrogs, wood frogs and even spring peepers have found a way to turn to ice in winter, their bodies nearly frozen solid, and still survive. With just a few warm spring days, they will thaw out and begin to do the things frogs normally do in the spring.

How do they do it? They create chemical "seeds" within their body cavities but outside the cells of their organs and other body tissues. When the temperature drops below freezing, ice crystals will form around the seeds so that the water inside the cells does not freeze. Up to two-thirds of a frog's body water can freeze, yet it can remain alive because its cells are unharmed.

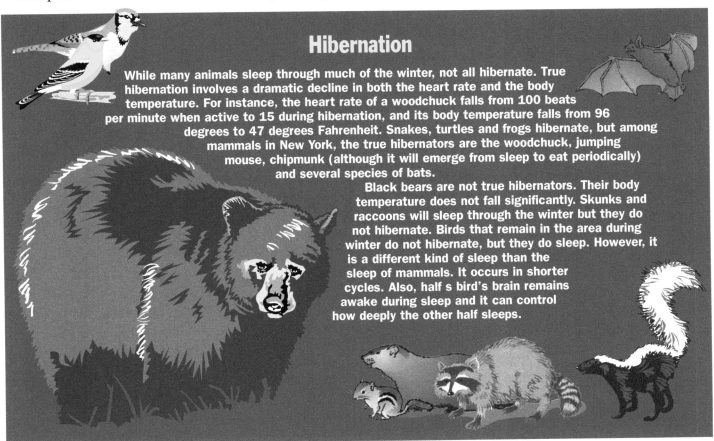

Hibernation

While many animals sleep through much of the winter, not all hibernate. True hibernation involves a dramatic decline in both the heart rate and the body temperature. For instance, the heart rate of a woodchuck falls from 100 beats per minute when active to 15 during hibernation, and its body temperature falls from 96 degrees to 47 degrees Fahrenheit. Snakes, turtles and frogs hibernate, but among mammals in New York, the true hibernators are the woodchuck, jumping mouse, chipmunk (although it will emerge from sleep to eat periodically) and several species of bats.

Black bears are not true hibernators. Their body temperature does not fall significantly. Skunks and raccoons will sleep through the winter but they do not hibernate. Birds that remain in the area during winter do not hibernate, but they do sleep. However, it is a different kind of sleep than the sleep of mammals. It occurs in shorter cycles. Also, half s bird's brain remains awake during sleep and it can control how deeply the other half sleeps.

It's not called the urban jungle for nothing. A city can be teeming with animals, from birds to bats to butterflies, and people who live there may be unaware of most.

That's because many animals that do choose to live where there are great concentrations of people eventually learn ways to live their lives without attracting notice.

There are some animals, though, that have the personality – and the agility – to live among people but to stay out of their way. Gray squirrels and pigeons can seem to be acrobats of city sidewalks as they avoid being trampled.

Still other animals thrive in cities because they are terrific survivors. Norway rats and German cockroaches, two species people especially dislike, have managed to survive despite the most intense efforts imaginable to eliminate them.

But even in urban areas, there can be rural landscapes in the form of city parks. They are often havens for animals. For birds especially, a park's greenery can be an oasis in the middle of a desert of concrete and steel. In fact, concentrations of some birds can be higher in a good-sized park than they are in the outlying rural areas.

That's especially true in spring and fall when birds migrate. They have to stop and rest periodically, and if they are flying over a densely populated area with lots of buildings and little greenery, a park, like Forest Park in Springfield, will stand out for them like the bull's-eye of a target.

Suburban towns can also harbor vast populations of wild animals. Some animals, such as deer, skunks, raccoons and opossums, are attracted by the easily obtained food provided by bird feeders, vegetable gardens, compost piles and trash cans.

Northampton, for instance, has a chronic problem with black bears. The city adjoins excellent rural bear habitat to

House sparrow nest in West Springfield

the north, and in the spring, when the bruins emerge from dormancy and food is still scarce, they invade the city in search of bird feeders and trash cans.

For some animals, the feeding opportunities in cities can be greater than in the deep forest. Peregrine falcons were originally a mountain species that vanished from the state due to use of the pesticide DDT, which was eventually banned. They would build their nests on cliff ledges and use that vantage point to spot prey, usually other birds, which they would attack in flight.

Falcons have since returned, but now they find the man-made cliffs of cities serve them just as well. They will nest on building ledges or on the girders of bridges and then hunt the canyons of the city for pigeons and other birds. In Springfield, falcons have nested regularly on an upper window ledge of a Main Street high-rise office building or on Memorial Bridge since 1989.

Peregrine falcon chick and mother at their nest on an office tower window ledge in Springfield

Gray squirrels have adapted to life in cities. In rural forests, they each claim territories of perhaps an acre or two and feed mainly on acorns and other nuts. In a city park, where food can be more plentiful, as many as 10 might live in a single acre. The urban squirrel's diet may include acorns, popcorn, peanuts and any other foods humans offer or leave behind.

Fall foliage in Williamsburg

Impressionist painters would not have gotten far without wildflowers.

Wildflowers were art before there was art – dashes of color on canvases of windblown meadows, craggy mountainsides and darkened forest floors.

Many seem to have been named by poets – Jack-in-the-pulpit, Queen Anne's lace, butter and eggs, yellow lady's slipper.

But as unplanned as a scattering of wildflowers may seem, where and when they bloom and the colors and shapes they take follow a general logic. Much of that logic has to do with helping each species of wildflower find its own place in the world.

If all wildflowers bloomed at the same time, grew in the same soil and sunlight conditions and attracted the same pollinators, the fierce competition would mean that only a few species would survive. So wildflowers evolved to be specialists. Some grow only in wet areas, some grow only in dry areas. Some thrive in valleys and others on mountainsides. Some can grow where there is a lot of sunlight, as in a meadow, while others can grow where there is little of it, as on a forest floor.

To further reduce competition, wildflowers also evolved to bloom at different times of year. Common violets bloom from April to June, but most asters don't bloom until September or October.

The beauty of wildflowers is not something created to please the human eye. It actually evolved to appeal to pollinators – butterflies,

Blue flag iris

Wild lupine

bees, ants, moths and even small birds, such as hummingbirds. The splashy and bold colors of some wildflowers are like neon signs outside a row of stores that aim to catch the eyes of passing customers. The fragrances the flowers give off and the sweet nectar produced inside the flowers are also intended as attractions to pollinators.

A wildflower must get the pollen that the male part of the flower creates to the female part of another wildflower of the same species so that seeds can be created. Pollinators are the pollen carriers.

If a butterfly visits a flower to feed on the nectar deep inside the flower, tiny grains of pollen may stick to it and be carried to the next flower it visits.

The varied shapes and colors of wildflowers also evolved to let a pollinator know exactly what kind of flower it is visiting. Most pollinators can recognize certain shapes and patterns of color, so if they like the nectar they find at a flower, they will know to visit that same type of flower again. In this way, pollen from a buttercup has a way of getting to another buttercup, rather than ending up on a wild geranium.

The bull's-eye shape of many flowers evolved to guide the pollinator to the nectar. "Here it is – right at the center," this shape seems to say. Other wildflowers have a shape like the end of a trumpet for the same reason. "The nectar is right inside here – you can't miss it," this shape seems to say.

In Massachusetts, there are nearly 1,800 to 2,000 species of wildflowers that can be found through the seasons.

Wildflower or weed?

There is no official definition for which is which. When people do not like a wildflower for some reason, they may think of it as a weed. Some people think dandelions are weeds because they can take over a lawn. But others like their colorful flowers and think of them as wildflowers. Oxeye daisies are a favorite wildflower of many, but they are thought of as unwanted weeds by dairy farmers because cows may refuse to graze on them.

Turk's-cap lily

Red clover

Fragrant water lily

Beautiful wildflowers

"Gather ye rosebuds while ye may," the poet urged.

A century ago, it was advice taken much too literally, as picking wildflowers was such a common and overindulged practice that it's a wonder some species survived at all.

Whether it was citizens gathering bouquets for household display or botanists and hobbyists picking for their personal collections, some of the rarest and most beautiful wildflowers in Massachusetts – from the orchids, like showy lady's slipper, to the state flower, the mayflower – were disappearing.

Finally, in 1935, the state Legislature took steps to outlaw unrestricted collecting of some rapidly disappearing species.

Today, awareness of endangered species laws and of conservation issues generally keeps indiscriminate

Butter and eggs

picking of wildflowers to a minimum. Few would say anything about someone plucking daisies or black-eyed Susans from a field, but collecting of any flower that appears the least bit uncommon would probably draw a disapproving gaze and possibly more.

In Massachusetts, there are more than 150 wildflowers and other plants on the state's list of endangered, threatened or special concern species.

In addition, the 1935 law protects azaleas, all orchids (including all five varieties of lady's slippers found in the state, endangered or not) and the mayflower.

While the fine for picking a mayflower, which is not on the state endangered list, is only $5 under the 1935 law, picking a cranefly orchid, which is endangered in the state, can bring a fine of $500 or more.

Buttercups in Hatfield

Bloom times for Western Massachusetts wildflowers
Observed times in Hampshire County
(Spring flowering times are typically later to the north and in higher elevations.)

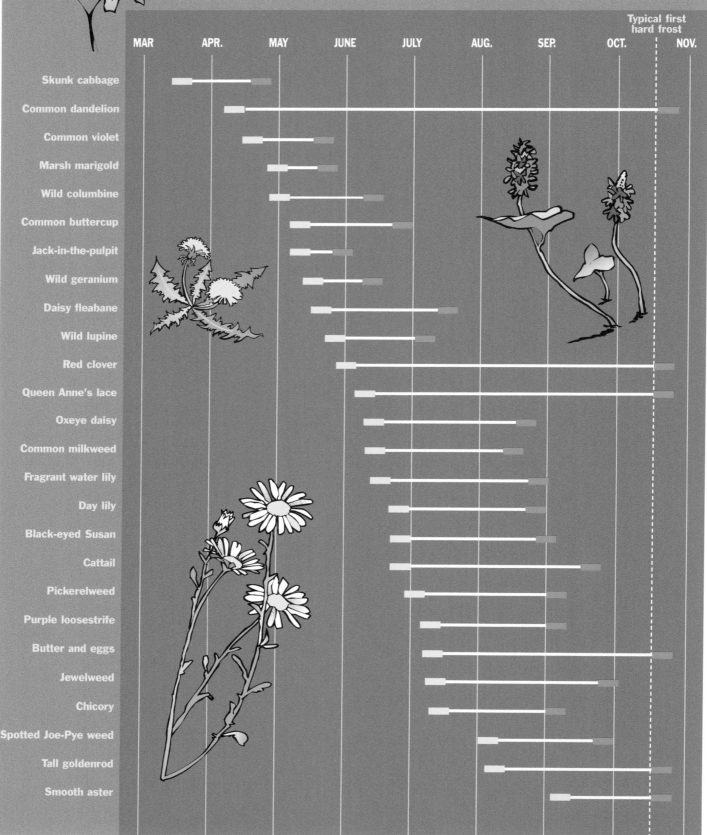

Typical first hard frost

	MAR	APR.	MAY	JUNE	JULY	AUG.	SEP.	OCT.	NOV.

Skunk cabbage
Common dandelion
Common violet
Marsh marigold
Wild columbine
Common buttercup
Jack-in-the-pulpit
Wild geranium
Daisy fleabane
Wild lupine
Red clover
Queen Anne's lace
Oxeye daisy
Common milkweed
Fragrant water lily
Day lily
Black-eyed Susan
Cattail
Pickerelweed
Purple loosestrife
Butter and eggs
Jewelweed
Chicory
Spotted Joe-Pye weed
Tall goldenrod
Smooth aster

CHECKLIST
Common wildflowers

Oxeye daisy
June – Aug.
1 – 3 in. wide
☐

Daisy fleabane
May – July
1 in. wide
☐

Queen Anne's lace
June – Oct.
2 – 6 in. wide
(cluster width)
☐

Fragrant water lily
June – Sept.
3 – 6 in. wide
☐

Tall goldenrod
Aug. – Oct.
.2 in. long
☐

Common dandelion
April – Oct.
1.5 in. wide
☐

Black-eyed Susan
June – Oct.
2 – 3 in. wide
☐

Common buttercup
May – June
1 in. wide
☐

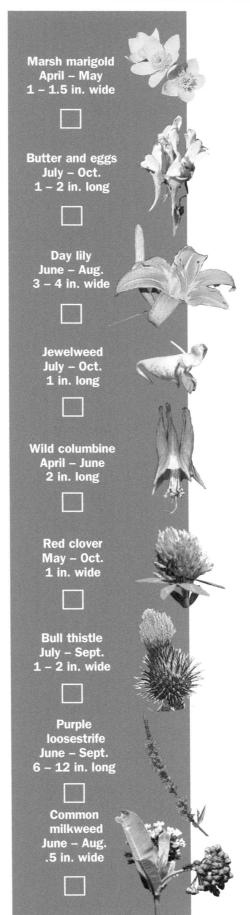

Marsh marigold
April – May
1 – 1.5 in. wide
☐

Butter and eggs
July – Oct.
1 – 2 in. long
☐

Day lily
June – Aug.
3 – 4 in. wide
☐

Jewelweed
July – Oct.
1 in. long
☐

Wild columbine
April – June
2 in. long
☐

Red clover
May – Oct.
1 in. wide
☐

Bull thistle
July – Sept.
1 – 2 in. wide
☐

Purple loosestrife
June – Sept.
6 – 12 in. long
☐

Common milkweed
June – Aug.
.5 in. wide
☐

Common blue violet
April – June
.5 – 1 in. wide
☐

Pickerelweed
July – Oct.
4 – 6 in.
☐

Spotted Joe-pye weed
Aug. – Sept.
4 – 5 in. wide
☐

Wild lupine
May – July
.7 in. long
☐

Wild geranium
May – June
1 – 2 in. wide
☐

Smooth aster
Sept. – Oct.
1 in. wide
☐

Skunk cabbage
March – May
3 – 6 in. long
☐

Cattail
June – Sept.
6 in. long
☐

Jack-in-the-pulpit
May – June
3 – 4 in. long
☐

A great spangled fritillary drinking in nectar at a flower

Flower power

The nectar of the gods. For hummingbirds, butterflies, bees and a range of other pollinating wildlife, the sweet liquid contained inside many flowers is truly that. Indeed, for many of them, flower nectar provides most of their fuel for energy.

Made up of a combination of water and different kinds of sugar, nectar is produced in parts of the flower called nectaries.

Plants need to spread their seeds to spread their species, so pollen from the male part – the stamen – of one plant must reach the female part – the pistil – of another to create a seed. Flowers produce nectar as a way to lure pollinating wildlife, such as butterflies and hummingbirds. Bits of pollen will stick to them while they are drinking, then they may visit another plant of the same kind for nectar and transfer the pollen to that plant's pistil as they linger to feed.

Butterflies drink nectar by sucking it in through a long narrow tube called a proboscis – like a drinking straw – that stays curled up at their mouth when they are not feeding.

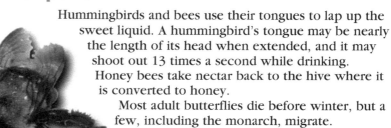

A bumblebee

Hummingbirds and bees use their tongues to lap up the sweet liquid. A hummingbird's tongue may be nearly the length of its head when extended, and it may shoot out 13 times a second while drinking. Honey bees take nectar back to the hive where it is converted to honey.

Most adult butterflies die before winter, but a few, including the monarch, migrate. Monarchs depend on the sugars in nectar to make what can be an 1,800 mile flight to their wintering grounds in Mexico. The monarchs born in late summer, in the last generation of the season, have a small area of fatty tissue by their abdomen in which they store fat that has been converted from the sugar of nectar. It is that fat that helps sustain them on their migration and through the winter.

Hummingbirds, which might beat their wings 50 times a second while hovering at a flower, have the highest heart rate of any animal, sometimes 1,200 beats per minute while feeding (compared to perhaps 180 for a human who is exercising.) To power that extreme metabolism, hummingbirds have to drink a lot of energy-rich nectar, sometimes taking in their body weight in the liquid each day.

A monarch butterfly feeding

Ruby-throated hummingbird, male

Pink lady's slipper

Wild columbine

Violets

Spotted touch-me-not

Milkweed buds

Mushrooms – A fungus among us

There is a saying: "There are old mushroom hunters and bold mushroom hunters, but there are no old, bold mushroom hunters."

After a warm rain, lawns can turn into bountiful mushroom factories, as puffballs, shaggy manes and boletes sprout seemingly overnight. One may be tempted to look on these fungal colonies (a mushroom is indeed only an elaborate fungus) as a free source of something you would have to otherwise pay for in a supermarket. But experts warn against it, given that so many are poisonous.

There may be several thousand species of mushrooms to be found in Massacusetts, including some that are deadly. There may be 10,000 species of mushrooms growing throughout North America, of which about 250 are considered edible, and about the same number are known to be poisonous, sickening or even capable of killing those who eat them. The rest are, to varying degrees, still mysteries.

Among the poisonous mushrooms, there are about 10 North American varieties that are considered deadly. And among those, the most feared is Amanita phalloides, the "death cap," which, although rare, has been found growing in suburban yards in the Northeast and elsewhere.

Its name is not hype. Eating just an ounce can be fatal.

Compounding the problem is that there are some poisonous mushrooms that can look very much like edible varieties. For instance, the destroying angel, which is deadly poisonous, can look almost identical to a type of common meadow mushroom.

The rule of thumb is that unless you know it, don't eat it.

Death cap mushroom, 3 in. tall

Orange oak bolete

Reg-veil amanita

Fly agaric

Ling chih

Russula Emetica

Even living within the heart of a city, you don't have to travel far in Massachusetts to find a rural landscape in the form of a state park.

The state oversees 450,000 acres of forests, beaches, bike trails, lakes, ponds, picnic areas, ski trails, streams, camping areas, old-growth trees, waterfalls, lodges, cabins, fishing spots, hiking trails and rivers.

From Cape Cod sunsets to dawns atop Mount Greylock, the beautiful scenery doesn't seem to stop.

Some notable state forests and parks in Western Massachusetts

Skinner State Park in Hadley is nearly 400 acres on Mt. Holyoke. At the top is the Mt. Holyoke Summit House which offers a commanding view of the Connecticut River Valley. The summit is accessible by car or by the many hiking trails.

Mt. Sugarloaf State Reservation in South Deerfield, with 533 acres, also offers a fine view of the Connecticut River Valley from atop the summit, which can be reached by car or foot.

Wahconah Falls in Wahconah Falls State Park in Dalton

Mt. Greylock State Reservation is 12,500 acres in Lanesborough surrounding the state's highest peak, Mt. Greylock, at 3,491 feet. The park has nearly 70 miles of trails as well as an 11.5 mile section of the Appalachian Trail. Atop the summit is Bascom Lodge, which offers rooms and meals with a spectacular view.

Bash Bish Falls State Park in Mount Washington, at 200 acres, has as its centerpiece Bash Bish Falls, the highest single-drop waterfall in the state at 60 feet. The falls can be reached via a half-mile trail. There are a series of gorges and ravines along the Bash Bish Brook and the park is adjacent to the much larger (4,169 acre) Mt. Washington State Forest.

Mohawk Trail State Forest is made up of more than 6,400 acres in Charlemont, Hawley and Savoy. It has 47 campsites, six overnight log cabins and 18 miles of rivers and streams for fishing. The park is named for a historic Native American foot path, the Mahican-Mohawk trail, sections of which are open for hiking.

October Mountain State Forest has nearly 16,500 acres in Washington, Becket, Lee and Lenox. The largest state park in Massachusetts and in the heart of the Berkshires, it contains 47 campsites, a home base to visit the Tanglewood Music Festival, Jacob's Pillow, Stockbridge Playhouse and the Berkshire Museum. The park also includes a section of the Appalachian Trail.

Parks and gardens

The greenery of a park is as necessary to the vitality of a city as fresh air and sunshine are to the health of its residents.

Indeed, the greenery and other color provided by parks as well as street trees, window boxes, median planters and private landscaping all enhance the sense of nature amid the city.

Springfield's Forest Park, designed by renowned landscape architect Frederick Law Olmsted, covers 735 acres and includes a zoo, hiking trails, tennis courts, baseball fields and the nation's first, municipally owned public swimming pool. Look Park in Northampton (157 acres) and Stanley Park in Westfield (300 acres) are also gems for their communities.

Bringing farming into the city has been the accomplishment of community gardens, an idea that first took root

The community garden in Northampton

in the United States in Detroit in the 1890's as a way to give the unemployed something to do.

The idea caught on and other cities soon began similar programs. However, during World War I, such gardens became an important source of fruits and vegetables in a time when there were severe food shortages across Europe. During the Great Depression, when money became scarce, growing your own food became a necessity for many. And During World War II, "victory gardens" again became a way to make up for widespread food shortages. In 1944 alone, such gardens provided 42% of the nation's vegetables.

In the 1970's, there was a revival of interest in community gardens rising out of two popular movements – environmentalism and urban activism. Today, it's estimated there are nearly 18,000 community gardens in North America.

Vacant lots as accidental gardens

A patch of earth in a city landscape is a window of opportunity for nature.

Examine any recently cleared vacant lot in a city, and then look at it a year or two later. Completely ignored, subjected to litter and pollution, given no ration of water but what the skies provide, this forgotten piece of property is likely to become a teeming garden of wildflowers and other plants in that time, an isle of greenery amid a sea of concrete and asphalt.

Typically, each spring and summer dozens of plants will manage to grow and flower there, revealing a spectrum of colors through the seasons – among them butter and eggs, Queen Anne's lace, phlox, spurge, dock, yarrow, clover, thistle, mullein, bittersweet, peppergrass, milkweed, ragweed and primrose.

In these urban lots, plants tend to stake out their own territories – phlox and peppergrass over here, thistles and spurge over there, almost as if they were deliberately planted in sections. That's often nature's pattern, a characteristic of a site that is relatively young. When a lot is first cleared, one plant will get established and the seeds will drop around it, so that it will spread out from there, colonizing the area immediately around it. A little farther away, another plant will be doing the same thing.

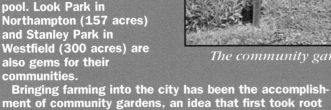
A vacant lot

In the first year, you will typically find plants popping up like mullein and Queen Anne's lace. They don't need a season of cold before they germinate. That's one of the reasons they are so prolific and they become established so quickly.

How do plants find their way into these isolated urban sites in the first place? It's because their seeds are expert travelers. Some arrive in bird droppings or when birds drop them in flight. Butterflies and other pollinators also bring some in, and many are blown in by the wind. In some cases, people carry them in. They may rub against a plant, such as milkweed or thistle, and the seeds might stick to their clothes and later drop to the ground.

Eventually, tree saplings will take root, species such as trees-of-heaven or mulberry trees. Soon, the growing trees will shade out many sun-loving species of ground plants and a different group of shade-tolerant plants will find their way into the mix. And, as often happens in an urban area, city workers may eventually cut these "weed trees" before they grow so tall that their roots buckle the nearby sidewalks or streets. They may even clear the plant growth. Then the lot is back to being a blank canvas on which nature is always willing to paint.

Henry David Thoreau, the philosopher, was supposedly able to look out his back door in Concord in the mid-1800s and see all the way to Mount Monadnock in New Hampshire because there were so few trees to block his view.

In fact, in the early 1800s Massachusetts may have looked much like a farm state in the Midwest. Farm fields, barren of trees, stretched from horizon to horizon in many places in Massachusetts. Only about a fifth of the state was forested.

Native Americans who lived in New England found they could more easily hunt animals in open areas than in thick forests, so they burned away many of the trees. And when Europeans settled in Massachusetts, they cleared more of the trees to create farm fields.

After the Civil War, though, many farmers in New England decided to leave their farms because they found they could not make a profit due to competition from farmers in the Midwest. Some moved west, seeking better land. Others moved to cities, seeking other kinds of jobs. Gradually, open land in the state began to grow back into forests.

Today, Massachusetts ranks eighth among all states in the percent of the state's land that is forested, some 63 percent, even though it ranks third among all states in population density (about 810 people per square mile). About 82 percent of Franklin County, 81 percent of Berkshire County, 72 percent of Hampshire County and 64 percent of Hampden County is forested.

Surely, there are billions of trees in the state – too many trees to possibly count. Not true. Just as it takes a census of people periodically, the federal government also takes an inventory of trees. In 2010, it was estimated there were 1.56 billion trees in the state that are at least one inch in diameter at breast height.

Massachusetts has a tremendous diversity of tree species in its forests – fir, spruce, hemlock, beech, red maple, white pine, red oak, green ash. Farther north in New England, you will find mainly "coniferous" trees – evergreen trees bearing cones, such as pines and hemlocks. Farther south in New England and in the mid-Atlantic states, you will find mainly "deciduous" trees, leaf-bearing trees, such as oaks and maples. Massachusetts lies between these two zones and has many varieties of both coniferous and deciduous trees.

Maple sugaring

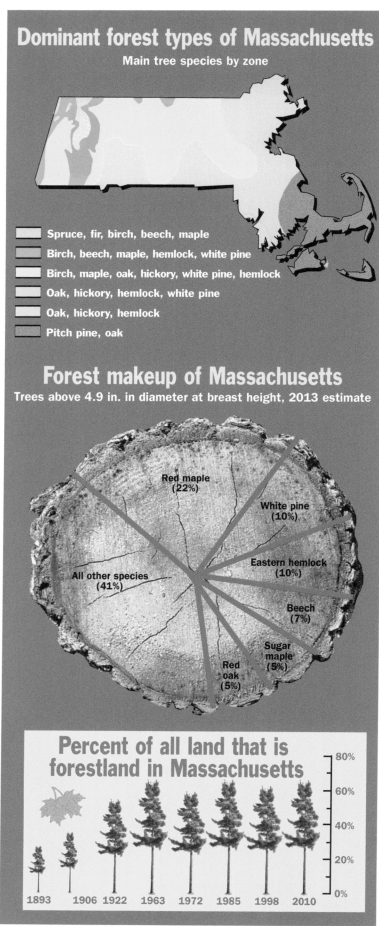

Dominant forest types of Massachusetts
Main tree species by zone

- Spruce, fir, birch, beech, maple
- Birch, beech, maple, hemlock, white pine
- Birch, maple, oak, hickory, white pine, hemlock
- Oak, hickory, hemlock, white pine
- Oak, hickory, hemlock
- Pitch pine, oak

Forest makeup of Massachusetts
Trees above 4.9 in. in diameter at breast height, 2013 estimate

- Red maple (22%)
- White pine (10%)
- Eastern hemlock (10%)
- Beech (7%)
- Sugar maple (5%)
- Red oak (5%)
- All other species (41%)

Percent of all land that is forestland in Massachusetts

80%
60%
40%
20%
0%

1893   1906   1922   1963   1972   1985   1998   2010

CHECKLIST
Common trees

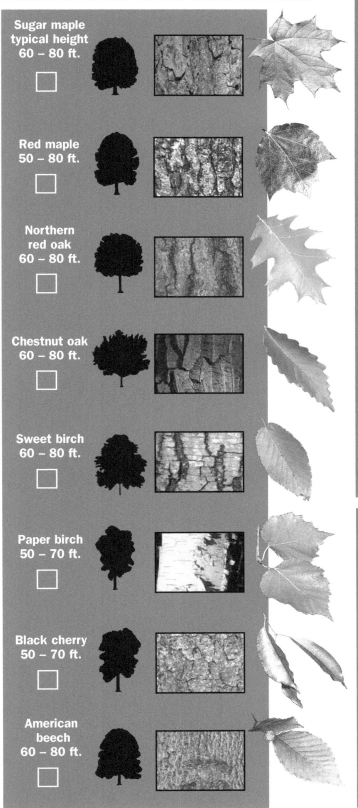

Sugar maple
typical height
60 – 80 ft.
☐

Red maple
50 – 80 ft.
☐

Northern red oak
60 – 80 ft.
☐

Chestnut oak
60 – 80 ft.
☐

Sweet birch
60 – 80 ft.
☐

Paper birch
50 – 70 ft.
☐

Black cherry
50 – 70 ft.
☐

American beech
60 – 80 ft.
☐

Shagbark hickory
70 – 120 ft.
☐

Green ash
40 – 60 ft.
☐

Weeping willow
30 – 50 ft.
☐

Eastern white pine
70 – 100 ft.
☐

Pitch pine
50 – 70 ft.
☐

Eastern hemlock
60 – 80 ft.
☐

Street trees

Honeylocust
50 – 80 ft.
☐

Norway maple
40 – 60 ft.
☐

London planetree
70 – 90 ft.
☐

Apple

Red maple

Sugar maple

Seed science

The apple doesn't fall far from the tree, the saying goes. However, for a species of tree to survive and spread, there has to be a way for the seeds to travel some distance to new locations.

The seeds of an apple tree are contained in the apple and when animals eat the lucious fruits, they inadvertently provide a way for the seeds to travel to a new place – usually in their digestive tract. When the animal finally passes solid wastes, the seeds encased in a hard shell end up on the ground, ready to take root, amid ready-made fertilizer.

Some trees, like red and sugar maples, produce winged seeds that travel on the wind to distant places like miniature helicopters. Other trees, like American beeches, produce tasty nuts (tasty to humans also) that are seeds as well. The acorns of oak trees are also seeds.

Coniferous trees, like pines, hemlocks and spruces, produce edible cones with the seeds inside. When a squirrel or other cone-eating animal carries the cone a distance to eat it, the seeds have a chance to travel too.

Eastern white pine

Norway Spruce

Eastern hemlock

American beech

Pitch pine

Northern red oak

Yellow birch

An acorn from a northern red oak pushes out a taproot

Acorn Ecology

The tiny acorns that litter the ground on hiking trails in the fall can be the key to survival for many forms of wildlife in a forest ecosystem. After all, mighty oaks from little acorns grow. And on little acorns a range of animals feed, including black bears, deer, turkeys, squirrels, chipmunks, mice, blue jays and vaious insects. And many of the animals that don't feed on acorns feed on animals that do. The nut-eating animals are often prey for larger animals, such as foxes, coyotes, bobcats, hawks and owls.

However, if all the acorns that fell in autumn got eaten, there would be no mighty oaks, and if there were no mighty oaks, the populations of all those animals that depend on acorns, either directly or indirectly, would be in trouble. So oaks have evolved to have a fascinating strategy that ensures that both oaks and animals survive.

Oaks have years when they produce a huge crop of acorns, called mast years. For oaks, mast years occur every three to five years on average. But in the years between mast years, oaks may produce few if any acorns. That way, the populations of the acorn-eating animals have less food in the in-between years and can never grow so large that all the acorns get eaten in the mast years. That guarantees new oaks will be able to take root while allowing the animals that depend on acorns to survive.

But here is the fascinating part. If one oak had a mast year and the oak beside it did not, this process would not

An acorn still on the branch

work. Acorn eaters would still have enough food that their populations would grow without limit, and in mast years, all the acorns might get eaten. But that doesn't happen.

In one of the great mysteries of nature, oaks, and other nut-bearing trees, have evolved so that somehow mast years occur at the same time for trees of that species over a vast area, sometimes thousands of square miles. That means the population of the oaks and the animals that eat acorns and other nuts remain in balance, and all have a chance to survive.

Oaks can't communicate with each other, as far as anyone knows. So how do they all agree to grow so many acorns at the same time? One leading theory is that variations in seasonal temperature, especially in the spring, trigger trees over a large area to produce large or small crops of nuts. One study of oaks in California found that in warm, dry Aprils, acorn production tended to be high in the fall.

An acorn that drops to the ground in autumn will grow a main root, called a taproot, that pushes down into the soil once temperatures warm in the spring. Within a week the root may be several inches long. Within another week, a stem may begin to grow upward and leaves will soon appear on the stem.

Because so many acorns are eaten or do not fall in a place where they can germinate, it may take 500 acorns to produce one oak seedling that reaches a year old.

Let's face it. Dinosaurs, extinct though they are, live in the limelight. Their spectacular size has made them media stars.

However, the tallest known dinosaur, Ultrasaurus, stood a mere 60 feet high, less than half the height of Pinus strobus, which managed to outlive the dinosaurs, surviving in Western Massachusetts even today. At more than 170 feet, the majestic height of the eastern white pine (as this towering species is also known), like that of other tall trees of the region, is something most of us take for granted.

White pines are the tallest trees in New England and in the East generally. In the Great Smoky Mountains National Park, there is a pine 188.8 feet high. However in this region, a white pine that exceeds 170 feet can be a champion. For years, the champion white pines for the Northeast were found in Cornwall, Conn., the so-called "Cathedral Pines." One in the stand measured 172 feet. However, tornadoes toppled the stand in 1989, and the title moved to pines in the Mohawk Trail State Forest in northern Berkshire County.

The so-called "Jake Swamp Pine" in that forest, close to Route 2, is the tallest accurately measured tree in New England. It has been now reached a height of 172.5 feet. Mohawk Trail State Forest is a breeding ground for tall wood of all kinds, boasting the tallest red maple (124 feet), American beech (128 feet), sugar maple (134 feet) and white ash (152 feet) in New England.

There is at least one national champion in the region. In Buckland, in the Buckland State Forest, there is a Norway spruce that is 150.5 feet, the tallest of its species in the nation. In the same state forest, there is also a European larch that is 146 feet, the tallest of its species in New England.

The Ice Glen in Stockbridge is a protected ravine that has been allowed to grow wild over the decades and it contains several champion trees. An eastern hemlock in the Ice Glen, measures 137 feet, the tallest of its species in New England. And a shagbark hickory in the Ice Glen stands 135 feet tall, also a New England champion.

In Springfield's Forest Park, there are two state champions – a pitch pine standing 102 feet tall and a black birch measuring 108 feet tall.

In the Connecticut River Valley, the soil was laid down by centuries of regular flooding. So it is often deep, rich

Eastern white pine at the William Cullen Bryant Homestead in Cummington

and sandy, which can be ideal growing conditions for tall trees. There are several trees in the river valley that are champions for the state or New England. They include:

● A butternut in Northampton, near the Mill River, that is 112 feet, the tallest of its species in New England.

● A sycamore in Easthampton, off Route 10, that is 137 feet, the tallest of its species in the state.

● A silver maple in Hatfield that is 117 feet, the tallest of its species in the state.

● A black locust in Northampton, near the Mill River, that is 114 feet, the tallest of its species in the state.

● A quaking aspen in Northampton, by Fitzgerald Lake, that is 88 feet, the tallest of its species in the state.

Is fall foliage just an accident?

Perhaps nature's most brilliant artistic touch, the scarlets and golds of autumn leaves may also be one of nature's most beautiful accidents.

The startling colors of fall are certainly admired by human beings. But the colors seem to defy one of nature's primary laws, since they are of no use to the trees themselves.

Most plants and animals have the features they have because those features help them survive in the world. But what use is a colorful leaf to a tree in autumn since the leaf is just about to die and fall to the ground?

Some scientists believe that autumn colors may have begun as an accident, the unexpected result of the chemical changes a tree goes through as it prepares to lose its leaves each fall.

But even if it was an accident, since this coloring causes no harm to the trees, there is no reason for trees to lose this process. If the coloring did cause harm, those species of trees whose leaves changed color might have become extinct by now, and only the trees whose leaves didn't change color might be alive today.

They are the silent observers of history. The oldest living trees of Massachusetts were alive when Native Americans dominated the region, when the Revolutionary War was fought and when electric lights first appeared.

Some of the state's ancient trees may be 500 and possibly 600 years old. However, very little virgin forest still exists in Massachusetts and New England. It's estimated there are about 1,100 acres of true old-growth forest left in Massachusetts, most of it in a few locations – the Deerfield and Cold river gorges, the Dunbar Brook watershed in Monroe State Forest, the western slopes of Mount Greylock, Mount Wachusett, and the areas around Mount Everett and Bash Bish Falls.

But if you think that the oldest trees in a forest are always the largest trees, you'd be wrong. Perhaps the oldest trees in Western Massachusetts are some of the most inconspicuous, usually growing to a height of less than 80 feet. They are black gum trees, also called black tupelo or pepperidge trees.

In Colonial times, much of New England's landscape was cleared for farming. In fact, by the early 1800s, only one acre in five in Massachusetts was forested. So only a small percentage of the region's trees have had a chance to achieve their greatest possible age. The advantage that black gums have had is that even in settled areas, they were often spared cutting by earlier loggers and farmers. The trees usually grew in swampy places and were not considered of any value.

Only in recent years have people who study old-growth trees recognized just how long this wetland species can survive. It had been thought that the oldest trees in the Northeast were no more than 550 years old. However, in New Hampshire, a black gum was found that is estimated to be 679 years old.

How do scientists determine the age of a tree? By counting its rings. A tree grows new wood around the outside of its trunk each year. In the late spring and early summer, when there is usually more moisture in the ground, the wood is light in appearance. In late summer and early fall, when conditions are usually drier, the wood being added tends to be darker. This alternating light and dark wood creates rings that can be seen when the tree falls in a storm or is cut.

To count the rings of a living tree, a scientist drills out a pencil-thin "core," a rod of wood extracted from the trunk on which the rings can be seen.

Black gum

There is no firm definition for an old-growth tree, but for many species, living 150 to 200 years can put them in that category. Most old-growth trees in New England today are found in the higher elevations of mountains or in places that people can't easily reach, such as on steep slopes. Among the long-lived species in Western Massachusetts, in addition to black gum trees, are eastern white pines, eastern hemlocks, white cedars, balsam firs, red spruces, sugar maples and American beeches.

While 500 years is an impressive life span for a tree in Western Massachusetts, it wouldn't raise an eyebrow in some other regions. There is a bald cypress in North Carolina that is estimated to be 1,622 years old, the champion for old growth in the eastern United States.

The champions for the nation, and perhaps the world, are bristlecone pines that grow on the barren, windy slopes of the southwestern United States. Some of those may be nearly 5,000 years old.

Old-growth trees of Western Massachusetts

Some notable stands

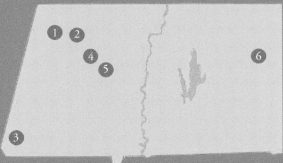

① Mount Greylock

ADAMS – Up to 500 acres of old-growth eastern hemlock, red spruce, sugar maple, red oak and white ash on the northern and western slopes of the mountain

② Mohawk Trail and Savoy Mountain state forests

SAVOY, FLORIDA AND CHARLEMONT – Nearly 700 acres of old-growth white pine, white ash, eastern hemlock, black birch, white oak and red oak

③ Mount Everett

MOUNT WASHINGTON – Perhaps 350 acres of old-growth pitch pine, eastern hemlock, white pine and red oak near the mountain's summit

⑥ Wachusett Mountain

PRINCETON – Perhaps 220 acres of old-growth red oak, American beech, eastern hemlock, yellow birch, sugar maple and red maple

⑤ Chesterfield Gorge

CHESTERFIELD – Perhaps 17 acres of old-growth eastern hemlock, sugar maple, black birch and yellow birch

④ William Cullen Bryant homestead

CUMMINGTON – About five acres of old-growth eastern hemlock, yellow birch, sugar maple, red maple and white ash

Imagine mountains as high as Mount Everest. Imagine erupting volcanoes. Imagine mile-high glaciers or frozen snowswept plains.

You are imagining landscapes that could have been seen in the Northeast at different times in its history.

Hard to believe? Not for geologists. They know that the appearance of every region on Earth has changed over time. They also know that now is a quiet time in the geologic cycle of Massachusetts and the Northeast, a momentary calm amid the violent upheavals that have marked the history of the region's landscape.

The Earth's crust, or surface layer, is made up of vast rock plates that form the continents and the ocean floor. There are about a dozen large plates and many smaller ones covering the Earth's surface, arranged like pieces in a jigsaw puzzle.

The crust under the oceans may have an average thickness of just four or five miles. The crust of the continental plates is about 25 miles thick on average.

Essentially, the plates "float" on a layer of denser rock, called the mantle, deeper within the Earth. The Earth's core has a temperature of perhaps 10,800 degrees Fahrenheit, and this great heat creates circulating currents

Layers of sedimentary rock in exposed bedrock by I-91 in Holyoke

of molten rock within the mantle, which slowly push the crustal plates along.

The plates typically move a few inches a year, sometimes coming together and sometimes moving apart. This is called continental drift.

Even at such a slow speed, though, when these massive plates push against each other, geologic fireworks happen. Mountains gradually rise into the air, volcanoes may erupt and earthquakes might rumble.

That's what's happening currently in the western United States. The Pacific and North American plates are slowly sliding by each other, grinding together along their edges. About 65 million years ago, when the plates were pushing right into each other, this process created the Rocky Mountains, which are considered "young" mountains. (Scientists believe the Earth is about 4.6 billion years old.)

Massachusetts is also part of the North American plate, but for nearly 200 million years this plate has been separating from the plate that is next to it on the east, the one on which Africa is located. So there are no strong geologic pressures on Massachusetts' part of the plate to create or enlarge mountains, or to produce volcanoes or sizable earthquakes, in the Northeast.

Boundaries of major plates of the Earth's crust

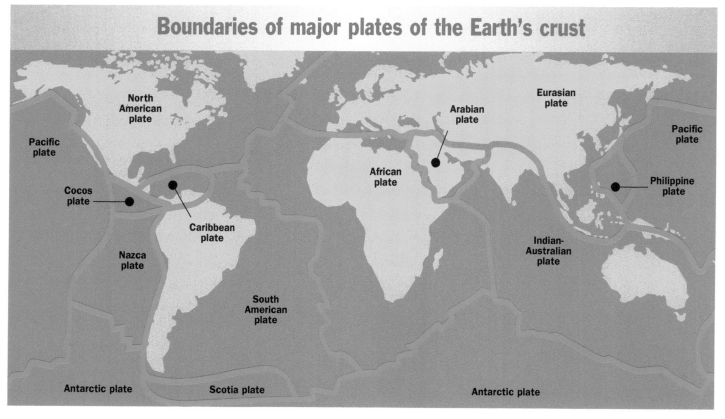

Drifting continents

At least three times in the last 500 million years, the East Coast of North America collided with other continental plates. These collisions did much to shape the landscape of Massachusetts.

Although continental plates may move only inches a year, their masses are so great and the forces pushing them along are so powerful that the process has long-lasting momentum.

Once the plates come together they may continue to push against each other for millions of years. This can create huge mountains in the region of the collision or, if the reaction of the land is violent, earthquakes or volcanoes.

500 million years ago

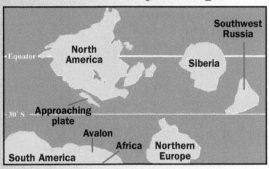

The land that will be Western Massachusetts lies south of the equator. Trees, plants and animals have not yet appeared on land. Primitive life is still developing in the oceans. The first fishlike creatures appear in water. Less than a foot in length, they lack jaws but they do have backbones, perhaps the first animals that are vertebrates.

The oxygen content of the Earth's atmosphere is rising sharply, but it will be another 100 million years before air-breathing land animals evolve.

Drifting north toward early North America is a plate covered with volcanoes that is about to collide with what will become the East Coast.

460 million years ago

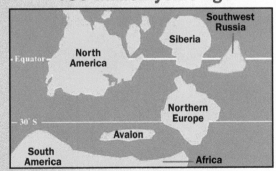

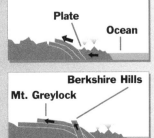

A plate drifting north collides with the North American coast, pushing up layers of rock that will form the Berkshire Hills. To the west, the collision pushes up the Taconic Mountains, including Mount Greylock. These peaks are higher than the Rockies are today, but gradually wind and rain will erode them.

Meanwhile, another plate, called Avalon by geologists, has broken free of the united African-South American continent and is drifting north.

380 million years ago

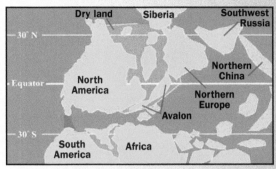

Avalon collides with North America, folding up layers of land like an accordion in New England. Huge mountains form in central Massachusetts. Past Avalon, out in the ocean, another plate is approaching. It holds what will one day be the African continent. Primitive fish fill the seas, and plants are starting to flourish on land.

300 million years ago

Africa collides with North America about 300 million years ago. Western Massachusetts now lies near the equator. All seven continents become joined in a single vast continent, called Pangaea by geologists.

200 million years ago

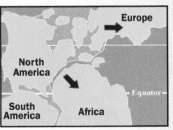

About 200 million years ago, Africa starts to pull away from North America. The stress creates deep tears in the land. As a result, a line of valleys forms that runs from Canada down to Georgia, including the Connecticut River Valley. They are called rift valleys today.

The first dinosaurs appear about 230 million years ago, but they are relatively small, just a few feet in height. Small mammals also appear.

However, the first birds and flowering plants will not appear for another 80 million years.

The rock cycle

Rocks have their own life cycle. It begins on the surface of the Earth when wind, rain and other natural forces break down existing rocks and other materials. The resulting particles become compressed and cemented together over the course of time to form new rocks.

When sand particles are turned to rock in this way, sandstone is the result. When clay, such as what is deposited on the bottom of a lake, is turned to rock, shale is the result. These two rocks are called sedimentary rocks, one of three categories of rocks along with metamorphic and igneous.

Eventually, sedimentary rocks, such as sandstone and shale, are buried by layers of other sedimentary rocks. With the heat and pressure deeper inside the Earth, they can become compressed further, making them harder still. That can turn them into metamorphic rocks, such as quartzite and slate.

Metamorphic rocks may eventually move to the surface due to earthquakes or the erosion of the land above them. But if metamorphic rocks move deeper into the Earth, the higher temperatures there can turn them to molten rock.

If this molten material hardens underground, it can become igneous rock, such as granite. If it surges up to the Earth's surface through a volcano as lava and hardens, it will become another form of igneous rock, such as basalt.

Harsh weather and the freezing and thawing through the seasons eventually disintegrate surface rocks. These rock particles may then become part of new sedimentary rocks, starting the cycle once again.

The rock collection

Sandstone
Sedimentary; formed from sand

Quartzite
Metamorphic; formed from sandstone

Shale
Sedimentary; formed from mud and clay

Limestone
Sedimentary; formed from minerals such as calcite

Siltstone
Sedimentary; formed from particles of silt, clay and sand

Slate
Metamorphic; formed from shale at low temperatures

Conglomerate
Sedimentary; formed from a mix of sand and pebbles

Dolomite
Sedimentary; formed from mud and limestone

Mineral or rock?

Minerals have crystalline structures, and they are usually made up of only a few chemical elements. For instance, diamond is made of carbon, and quartz is made of silicon and oxygen. Rocks, such as schist or granite, may be made up of combinations of minerals and bits of other rocks. While the minerals in it may have crystalline structures, the overall rock usually does not.

Schist
Metamorphic; often formed from shale at medium temperatures

Gneiss
Metamorphic; formed from igneous and sedimentary rocks

Quartz, a mineral

Granite
Igneous; formed when molten rock cools underground

The bedrock of Western Massachusetts

If you dig down through the loose dirt and rocks on the Earth's surface, you will eventually strike solid rock, called bedrock.

The bedrock of Western Massachusetts can be divided into two major zones: the Connecticut River Valley and the mountains and high hills outside the valley.

Much of the bedrock of the Berkshires Hills is gneiss and schist, older metamorphic rock, some of which is the original rock of the North American continent, perhaps a billion years old. There, and in the Pelham Hills, you might have to dig down only 4 or 5 feet through the surface soil, loose rock and gravel to reach the bedrock. Wind, rain and other erosive forces usually keep the depth to bedrock shallow in hilly or mountainous regions.

The bedrock of the flatter areas of the valley, of Springfield, Chicopee, Northampton and South Hadley, is mainly sedimentary rock, such as sandstone. But in some places, to reach this bedrock, you would have to dig through perhaps 200 feet of clay, soil and gravel. Over the years, periodic flooding of the Connecticut River and other rivers that have flowed through the ancient valley deposited layer upon layer of materials that buried the bedrock deeply.

Within the valley, though, are several lines of highlands, including the Holyoke Range. The bedrock of these highlands, of Mount Holyoke for example, is primarily igneous, such as basalt, which is hardened lava. It, too, lies closer to the surface than the bedrock of the valley lowlands.

The geologic zones

- Sandstone, conglomerate and shale (sedimentary)
- Schist, quartzite and phyllite (metamorphic)
- Limestone and dolomite (sedimentary
- Granite (igneous) and gneiss (metamorphic)
- Basalt and diabase (igneous)
- Gneiss and schist (metamorphic)

New England's landscape is not known for its volcanoes, for exploding mountain peaks and fiery rivers of lava. But once it was.

From inland Connecticut to coastal Maine can be found the remains of long-dead volcanoes. In fact, Mount Tom in Easthampton and Holyoke is the legacy of a particularly large eruption of lava.

Why are volcanoes only ancient history in this region? Look at any map showing the world's active volcanoes and it's clear most are found in those places where the vast plates that hold the continents and oceans are being jammed together or wrenched apart along their edges as they drift slowly over the Earth's surface.

Volcanoes are a natural result of these geologic upheavals. Where the Earth's dozen or so major crustal plates thin or are torn open along their edges, rock deeper in the Earth, which may have melted from the high pressure and temperature deeper in the Earth, can ooze to the surface as molten lava.

New England is now located in the middle of the North American plate, thousands of miles from its edges. But 500 million to 190 million years ago the land that would one day be New England could be found at various times along the edges of drifting plates. And erupting volcanoes were as common on those landscapes in those times as they are today in the U. S. Pacific Northwest, Alaska, Japan and other regions within the "Ring of Fire," a horseshoe-shaped zone encircling the Pacific Ocean where most of the world's 800 to 900 active volcanoes can be found.

Volcanoes can range from quiet, gentle oozes of lava coming from cracks or fissures in the crust to sudden, violent explosions that blow the tops off mountains and send plumes of ash miles into the atmosphere.

Evidence of ancient volcanoes in New England is not hard to find. It exists in the Connecticut River Valley around Holyoke and Deerfield. The eruptions took place about 200 million years ago. The Holyoke Range and the Pocumtuck Range to the north are what remains of those eruptions.

By all indications, the valley eruptions were quiet with

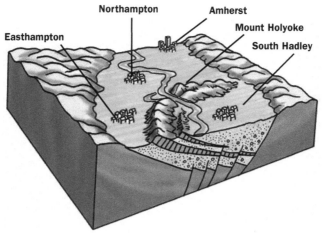

200 million years ago
Lava flows to surface in newly formed valley along a fault

Second smaller lava flow occurs some time later

200 to 140 million years ago
Valley gradually drops on the east along a fault

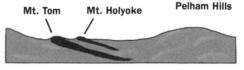

Today
Valley surface has eroded to reveal ancient tilted lava beds

gentle oozings of lava rather than violent eruptions, as they resulted from plates moving apart, not jamming together. But the sheer volume of lava that issued from cracks and fissures in the valley was impressive, say geologists.

One theory is that the lake of lava that formed may have been nearly 100 miles long, 30 miles wide and 500 feet thick in places.

What made the valley eruptions possible was a thinning of the Earth's crust. Some 200 million years ago, North America and Africa were joined along New England's coast, but they were about to start the process of pulling away from each other. The stress on the land ripped it apart in places. This is how the Connecticut River Valley formed. It is one of a series of "rift" valleys running from Canada down to Georgia.

The deep, newly formed valley allowed molten rock to reach the surface through cracks and fissures. The eruptions in Holyoke and Deerfield probably occurred around 200 million years ago. A second smaller eruption in Holyoke came later after the valley had filled in a bit.

The lava poured into the valley like molasses settling into a bowl. The molten rock, 2,000 degrees Fahrenheit or more, cooled into vast sheets.

From 200 million to 140 million years ago, the valley floor dropped gradually and significantly on the east side, tilting all the sheets partially up on their sides. Because the volcanic rock in these sheets was so much tougher than the rocks around it, millions of years of weathering have not eroded them as much as the surrounding rocks.

Today, the edges of these massive tilted sheets form Mount Tom, the Holyoke Range and the Pocumtuck Range above Deerfield.

As one drives along Interstate 91 through the Holyoke Range, one can see exposed rock, basalt that is nearly black, in those places along the roadside where the mountain was blasted away to allow the road through. It is in fact the hardened lava from the volcanic eruptions in the valley those millions of years ago.

In nature's catalogue of horrors, earthquakes are perhaps the most feared killer.

No other natural disaster kills large numbers of people with the regularity and suddenness of earthquakes. Of the world's 100 deadliest natural disasters of the 20th century, including famine caused by drought, a quarter were earthquakes, killing an estimated 1.5 million people.

To live in New England is to live largely – but not entirely – free of the threat of dangerous quakes. The most powerful earthquake of the last century in New England, which was centered near Ossipee, N.H., in 1940, was less than one-thousandth the strength of the earthquake that caused the deadly tsunami in the Indian Ocean in 2004.

The most active region in the world for earthquakes is the "Ring of Fire" surrounding the Pacific Ocean. Nearly 90 percent of the world's earthquakes occur in this zone, which sits atop a line of major active breaks or faults in the Earth's underlying bedrock.

New England and Western Massachusetts sit far from any major fault in the Earth's crust, and detectable earthquakes are dramatically fewer in number and weaker in power than those in the Ring of Fire.

The "Ring of Fire" with earthquake hotspots in red

most of which are so small they aren't felt. However, a half million ccur each year that can be dected by current instruments. Only about 140 destructive quakes – those with a magnitude six or greater – are recorded each year.

Earthquakes happen because the Earth's continental plates are moving perhaps a few inches a year. Where two plates are pushing together, pressure might build up for decades or centuries on this fault line, like a spring being compressed, until the rock on one side or the other gives way, causing a sudden and violent movement of land that sends out shock waves in all directions. This trembling of the ground is what we feel as the quake.

If New England is so far from the nearest plate boundary (in the mid-Atlantic, about 2,000 miles away), why does this region experience any earthquakes at all? Scientists aren't exactly sure, but one theory is that the six-state region, which was positioned on the edge of a continental plate early in its history, still has small, ancient faults in its underlying bedrock. If enough pressure builds up at those faults, they can produce small earthquakes.

That's not to say large earthquakes can't occur in New England. In 1755, a quake with an estimated magnitude of 6.2 struck off Cape Ann. Although centered 30 miles north of Boston, it nevertheless toppled chimneys throughout the city and knocked the weather vane off Faneuil Hall.

Perhaps a half dozen to a dozen measurable earthquakes occur in the six states each year. However, most are not even powerful enough near their epicenter to rattle a few dishes.

The intensity of earthquakes is measured on the Richter scale, so that a quake of magnitude four releases 30 times more energy than one of magnitude three, and one of magnitude three releases about 32 times more energy than one of magnitude two.

Globally, about two earthquakes occur each minute,

Over the years, Western Massachusetts has had its share of small quakes, generally under magnitude 3. From Oct. 2 to Oct. 25, 1994, there were nine quakes centered within 20 miles of Petersham. One registered 3.7 on the Richter scale, although the rest averaged about magnitude 2.6.

The destruction caused by the San Francisco earthquake of 1906, pictured below, was the greatest for any quake in U. S. history. The earthquake measured an estimated 7.8 on the Richter scale, nearly 40 times as powerful as estimates of the 1755 Cape Ann quake. The earthquake and the fires that burned for three days afterward left more than 250,000 homeless and killed between 450 and 700 people.

The largest earthquake ever recorded in the world hit Chile in 1960, registering 9.5 on the scale. The 2004 Indian Ocean earthquake, which measured 9.2, produced a massive tsunami, or tidal wave, that killed nearly 230,000 people when it came ashore in 14 countries. In places, the wave was 100 feet high.

A pair of Diplodocuses watch a Pterodactyl soar overhead, a scene that likely depicts a shoreline in what is now western North America in the late Jurassic Period

What began two centuries ago with a South Hadley farm boy's curiosity has become nothing less than a magnificent cultural obsession.

Dinosaurs. They could not be more alive today than if Triceratops and Diplodocus still walked the Earth.

The discovery by 12-year-old Pliny Moody of what appeared to be bird tracks in a slab of sandstone on his father's farm in 1802 was one of the first steps in a process that today finds dinosaurs as stars of museums, books and movies.

Because of the unusual geologic conditions in the Connecticut River Valley in the early age of dinosaurs some 200 million years ago, this valley became one of the richest sources of fossilized dinosaur tracks in the world. But more importantly, with Moody's discovery, it became the first. The valley is renowned for its dinosaur footprints.

It takes mud to make and preserve a dinosaur footprint, and in late Triassic and early Jurassic times Western Massachusetts was rich in mud.

Those 200 million years ago, the seven continents were joined together in a single supercontinent, called Pangaea by geologists, but the land was about to separate. What would become North America was joined on the east to Africa, but the two land masses were struggling to pull apart.

The stress on the land caused cracks

The rock slab containing dinosaur footprints found by Pliny Moody in 1802

to open in the land, and a line of valleys, called rift valleys, formed that extended from Canada down to Georgia, including the Connecticut River Valley. The steep sides of the valley might have been a mile high, and gravel and soil regularly washed down the valley walls during rainstorms, filling the lowlands with layers of mud. A dinosaur would leave a footprint in new mud, the mud would dry in the sun and then it would be buried by the next layer of mud from the next storm. Eventually, there would be layers of mud and prints underground that would slowly turn to rock over the centuries.

Within a few million years, the valley filled up and the heavy flow of mud largely stopped, ending the golden era of print-making locally.

Now we skip ahead 200 million years to 1802. Dinosaurs were extinct, and in fact no one yet knew they had ever existed. Pliny Moody, plowing a field in South Hadley, saw what he thought were bird tracks embedded in red sandstone. The slab of rock was dug up and eventually became a doorstep in the Moody home, a novelty to be shown to visitors. Many believe it is the first sample of fossilized dinosaur tracks deliberately collected.

Now we skip ahead 33 more

How dinosaur footprints were formed

The Connecticut River Valley about 190 to 200 million years ago

Erosion created a constant flow of sediments off surrounding mountains

River

Connecticut River Valley

Rift valleys

1. Tracks left by a dinosaur in soft mud after a rain storm might dry and harden in the hot sun over several days.

2. Another rain storm might wash a new layer of mud over the footprints, filling them in. Then this layer might fill with new footprints and harden in the sun.

3. Over time, layer would build upon layer, and the original tracks might be hundreds of feet underground, where they would turn to rock under the pressure.

years. A doctor in Greenfield, James Deane, saw what he thought were turkey tracks in the shale being used to pave sidewalks there in 1835. He contacted Edward Hitchcock, a minister, geologist and naturalist teaching at Amherst College – a moment that many point to as the formal beginning of the study of dinosaurs. However, no one imagined at the outset they were the tracks of such creatures.

Indeed, the Springfield Republican of November 18, 1837, spoke of the "the Giant Turkeys of Prof. Hitchcock."

Through his life, Hitchcock would collect or acquire nearly 1,100 rock slabs containing fossilized dinosaur tracks that were quarried in the Connecticut River Valley, including the Pliny Moody tracks, and he would dedicate his career to discovering what the ancient animals were that made them.

When mysterious fossilized bones began to be found in significant numbers in Europe in the 1840s, momentum began to grow that the bones and prints represented extinct animals that predated humans by millions of years. However, it was not until 1842 that an English naturalist, Richard Owen, used the word "dinosauria" (meaning "fearfully great lizards" in Greek) to describe these creatures.

Most of the prints Hitchcock found were from the era early in the evolution of dinosaurs, well before the largest and best known of their breed walked the Earth.

Dinosaur print from the Connecticut River Valley

The Hitchcock tracks, which are on display at Amherst College's Museum of Natural History, were made by relatively small dinosaurs with three toes on each foot. Most walked on two feet. However, some stood perhaps 10 to 12 feet high and walked on all four feet.

As dinosaur bones were increasingly found in other parts of the world, the fossilized tracks of the Connecticut River Valley – and Hitchcock – were largely forgotten. However, in the 1970s, there was a revival of interest in the tracks when scientists recognized tracks could tell things about the behavior of dinosaurs that bones could not. After all, tracks are the products of living dinosaurs going about their daily lives.

For instance, there had long been a belief that dinosaurs dragged their tails as they moved. Hitchcock's collected tracks were re-examined and only a small fraction showed tail marks, indicating most dinosaurs carried their tails in the air, something modern textbooks now depict.

In addition, because there were numerous tracks of the same species of dinosaurs on various slabs, it was concluded that some dinosaurs traveled in herds.

Tracks have been found in other locations in the world as well, and some show that dinosaurs would walk in groups with smaller dinosaurs in the middle, a defensive arrangement to protect the young.

Tracks can determine whether an animal carried its

legs directly under its body or pushed out to the sides, whether it walked pigeon-toed or waddled like a goose. They can also indicate how fast an animal was moving.

In the end, Hitchcock's impact on the study of dinosaurs was enormous and it continues today.

While dinosaur tracks can be found in New England, the fossilized bones of these ancient creatures rarely are, and the bones of large dinosaurs never have been. Great dinosaur skulls, the size of small cars, seem to regularly emerge from the rocks of Montana or North Dakota or Wyoming. No similar news has ever come from anywhere in New England.

Did the massive Stegosaurus ever walk the ground that is now Springfield? Did the fierce Tyrannosaurus rex hunt where Greenfield resides today?

Scientists who study dinosaurs say there is no doubt they did. However, it took a particular set of circumstances for a fossilized dinosaur bone to be created and it took another set of circumstances for it to survive to be found today. For a dinosaur bone or skeleton to be preserved as a fossil, the animal would have to die in a place where its remains would be covered up relatively quickly by sand or mud, such as by a lake or on a beach.

Over the years, minerals such as calcium in the sand or mud would settle into the cells of the bones, eventually hardening into rock. That means a rock would be created that had the exact shape and size of the original bone, and it would be embedded in the sand or mud

Dinosaur print from the Connecticut River Valley; Mud filled a track and then hardened, thus creating a track that projected out instead of in.

that had buried it. Eventually, the sand or mud would turn to rock, encasing the fossilized bone.

Over time, that rock would have to avoid being eroded away by wind or water, yet it would also have to be close enough to the surface today to be found by fossil hunters.

Those who hunt dinosaur fossils in New England, and in much of the eastern United States for that matter, are at a disadvantage compared to fossil hunters in the West. In arid regions of the West, like parts of Montana and the Dakotas, wind and water are constantly wearing down regions of sedimentary rock, such as shale or sandstone, which may contain fossils. Fossils that sat hundreds of feet below the ground are eventually brought to the surface by this constant erosion.

In the East, there may be thousands of complete dinosaur skeletons to be found, but because the region is relatively wet, there are thick forests that have deposited layer upon layer of leaves and dead wood to keep those fossils covered. At the same time, the East does not have the scouring winds blowing over broad plains that wear down the landscape, exposing fossils. And if that is not enough, so much of the East is developed that these additional layers roads, homes and businesses have helped to hide what fossils might be found here.

For an animal's bones to be buried so that the fossilization process can begin, the animal has to die in a place onto which mud or sand is flowing. Only in the early

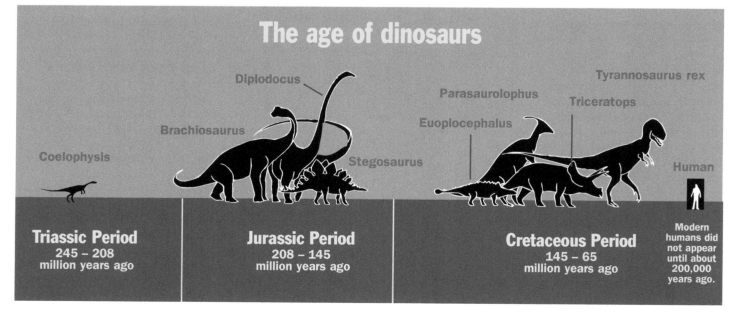

The age of dinosaurs

Coelophysis

Brachiosaurus

Diplodocus

Stegosaurus

Euoplocephalus

Parasaurolophus

Triceratops

Tyrannosaurus rex

Human

Triassic Period
245 – 208
million years ago

Jurassic Period
208 – 145
million years ago

Cretaceous Period
145 – 65
million years ago

Modern humans did not appear until about 200,000 years ago.

part of the age of dinosaurs, about 200 million years ago, were mud, sand and other sediments flowing heavily into the Connecticut River Valley. By 150 million years ago, when 80-foot-long creatures like Brachiosaurus roamed the land, the Connecticut River Valley had completely filled in and the region had been worn down to a flat plain. There was little new sediment, such as mud or gravel, being deposited on the surface to capture the bones or prints of this giant.

When a dinosaur died, its bones likely deteriorated on the surface before they could be fossilized. That means there was almost no evidence of those times left for present day geologists and paleontologists to find.

However, none of this means fossilized dinosaur bones have never been found in New England. Indeed, one of the most famous finds in the region, a partial skeleton of a small dinosaur called Podokesaurus, was made very near Mount Holyoke College by Mignon Talbot, a geology professor at the college known for her interest in dinosaurs. In 1910, she found the skeleton embedded in the side of a sandstone boulder on a farm.

Unfortunately, the fossil was destroyed in a 1917 fire at the college. However, casts of it had been made and today one survives at the Amherst College Museum of Natural History. Scientists believe the Podokesaurus was about six feet long, that it was a meat eater and, based on the foot bones, it may have been able to run

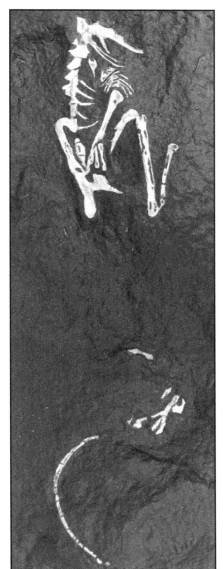

Cast of the fossilized bones found by Mignon Talbot

nine to 12 miles per hour.

Just south of Springfield, in Manchester, Conn., in the 1880s, a single quarry produced an unprecedented three skeletons of dinosaurs from the early Jurassic, about 200 million years ago. The bones were found by workmen in sandstone blocks being prepared for construction. One skeleton remains the most complete and best-preserved skeleton of a prosauropod dinosaur ever found in North America.

Prosauropods were plant eaters. They were typically 23 to 30 feet in length, and many could stand to reach leaves and fruits as high as 13 feet above the ground. They had long necks and tails, small heads and simple teeth.

Interestingly, rock from the quarry was being used for supports for a bridge being constructed in South Manchester, and it was believed one block used in the bridge held one or more of the missing bones from one of the discovered skeletons. Obviously a bridge couldn't be taken down just to recover some old fossils, but curators at the Peabody Museum of Natural History at Yale kept track of the bridge for more than 80 years, and when it was finally demolished in 1969, researchers from the museum were there to search for the missing block.

They examined nearly 400 sandstone blocks over a two-day period, and finally did find the block containing one of the missing bones. It has since been reunited with the original skeleton at the museum.

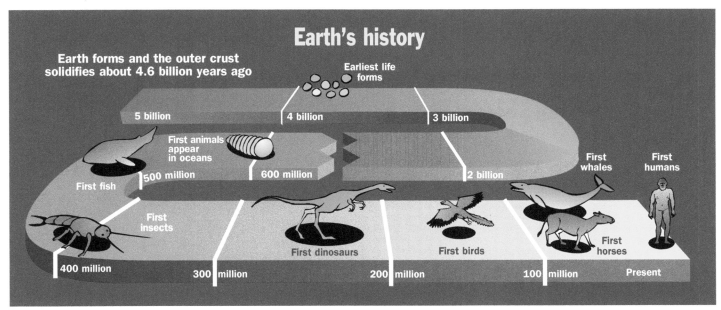

Earth's history

Earth forms and the outer crust solidifies about 4.6 billion years ago

Earliest life forms

5 billion

4 billion

3 billion

First animals appear in oceans

500 million

600 million

2 billion

First fish

First whales

First humans

First insects

First dinosaurs

First birds

First horses

400 million

300 million

200 million

100 million

Present

It was the dead of winter even in the heart of summer. It was the ice age.

During the last two million years, there have been four major advances of continental glaciers into the northern United States from centers in Canada.

The most recent ice age began about 70,000 years ago when a glacier that had formed in eastern Canada slowly expanded, eventually covering most of the Northeast United States. In some places, the ice was more than a mile thick. The glacier, called by geologists the Laurentide ice sheet, also spread west, covering most of Canada and the northernmost United States from the Rocky Mountains eastward. It did not begin to melt away from the Northeast until about 21,500 years ago.

Glaciers form when the climate of a region cools enough so that snow builds up in winter faster than it melts in summer. Just as a snowball turns to an ice ball if you squeeze it hard enough, snow, if it continues to pile up, can eventually become so compressed that much of it turns to ice, especially at the bottom of the pile.

The increase in snow and ice year after year can create a mound of ice so high that the weight of it causes the ice to begin to spread slowly outward at the bottom, like thick maple syrup flowing on a tabletop – except at a much slower pace. On average, a glacier may advance a few feet a day. But at times, it may barely move and at other times it may surge forward several hundred feet in a day.

Even at this relatively slow speed, though, a glacier can move a great distance over thousands of years, as it did during the last ice age.

Much of the landscape of Massachusetts was shaped by the glaciers that reached down into the Northeast. If there had been no glaciers, Cape Cod, Nantucket and Martha's Vineyard would not exist today.

A glacier can be like a vacuum cleaner, drawing up into the ice the rocks and boulders that it finds in its path or that it digs out of the bedrock as it advances. When at last the climate warms enough so that a glacier begins to melt back, all the debris trapped in the ice is dropped to the ground, and that is why much of Massachusetts has so many loose rocks and boulders on its surface.

A glacier can also be like a bulldozer, widening and deepening valleys as it moves. Like a bulldozer, it may also push rocks and boulders along in front of it.

A family of woolly mammoths during the ice age.

When the ice melts, the meltwater may fill the valleys it dug, forming lakes. And the debris that was pushed along at the front edge of the glacier may be left in long piles called moraines.

The last glacier to cover the Northeast stopped and began to melt back when it reached what is today Long Island and the Massachusetts islands. In fact, the moraines the glacier left sat high enough that when sea level stabilized, Long Island, Cape Cod, Nantucket and Martha's Vineyard were created.

Most of Western Massachusetts was not free of ice until about 13,500 years ago. However, once the ice was gone from the area, the landscape did not immediately spring back to life. It was probably frozen, barren and blanketed with snow much of the year, a wasteland covered with glacial debris. Low tundra vegetation, similar to what you would see near the Arctic today, grew on it for centuries. However, many of the animals and plants that are native to the region today gradually began to spread their range from the south into this area. The animals included deer, skunks, foxes and black bears.

The first human beings arriving in the Northeast after the last ice age may have encountered very cold conditions indeed.

Ice retreat

By 21,500 years ago, the most recent glacier to cover New England had reached its southernmost limit at about Long Island and begun to melt back. By 11,000 years ago, it had retreated into Canada.

11,000 years ago

13,000 years ago

14,000 years ago

21,500 years ago

North America's last glacier

Cordilleran ice sheet

Laurentide ice sheet

THE FUTURE CANADA

THE FUTURE UNITED STATES

Ice age detectives

When a glacier melts, it leaves behind nothing of itself to tell geologists how it advanced. It does leave indirect clues, though.

As a glacier moves over the land, it carries rocks in its bottom layers that scratch the exposed bedrock over which the ice passes.

Atop Mount Washington in New Hampshire, the highest peak in New England at more than a mile above sea level, geologists have found scratch marks on exposed bedrock that is evidence that a glacier passed over the mountain peak.

That tells them the ice was at least that high in places.

As a glacier advances, it also

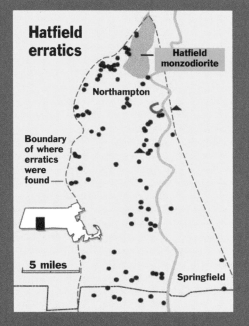

Hatfield erratics

Hatfield monzodiorite

Northampton

Boundary of where erratics were found

5 miles

Springfield

picks up rocks in one area and drops them in another. The rocks are called erratics. Occasionally, the ice picks up bits of bedrock in an area with a kind of bedrock found almost nowhere else in that region. By mapping where these erratics are dropped, a scattering of rocks called a boulder train, geologists can tell the direction the glacier traveled.

For instance, in Hatfield, there is an area of igneous bedrock, monzodiorite. Rocks of this type have been found in a fan-shaped area that extends more than 20 miles to the south, marking the path of the glacier through that region.

Animals of the ice age

Giant cats with teeth like daggers. Shaggy-coated, long-tusked creatures that looked like elephants. Beavers larger than a man. Bison weighing a ton and a half. Musk oxen, ground sloths, wild pigs and caribou.

Some of the animals that roamed North America as the last ice age ended may have seemed to belong more to the age of dinosaurs. The much colder climate of the northern regions 20,000 years ago provided a home to a different group of animals than one sees today, creatures that were able to survive on a frozen landscape.

However, as the ice melted away and the climate warmed, many of the same animals found in the Northeast today, including skunks, white-tailed deer,

opossums, raccoons and black bears, moved into the region from warmer areas to the south.

It's believed the first humans arrived in North America between 13,000 and 19,000 years ago as the last ice age was ending. They may have hunted the largest of the ancient ice age animals to extinction in a matter of just 2,000 or 3,000 years, including the woolly mammoths and mastodons.

Saber-toothed cats are believed to have lived throughout North and South America. These huge predators, which also hunted mammoths and mastodons, probably went extinct soon after the ice age ended, when their primary prey disappeared.

Woolly mammoth
Height: 9 to 11 feet at the shoulder
Weight: 8,000 to 12,000 pounds

American mastodon
Height: 8 to 10 feet at the shoulder
Weight: 8,000 to 10,000 pounds

Saber-toothed cat
Length: 6 to 8 feet
Weight: 400 to 500 pounds

Lake Hitchcock

You will not find Lake Hitchcock on any Rand McNally map of the Connecticut River Valley. Not unless it is a version that is 14,000 years old.

But in its time, the massive lake, which formed as the last ice age ended, stretched from well up into Vermont to well down into Connecticut. Despite its disappearance all those millennia ago, it still defines much about the valley landscape in Massachusetts today, from where good farm land can be found to where stone walls can be seen running along country roads.

The valley is perhaps 200 million years old, and common sense says that a river always meandered through it, draining the surrounding land. During a series of ice ages, though, New England was periodically covered over with glacial ice, shutting down the river. The last

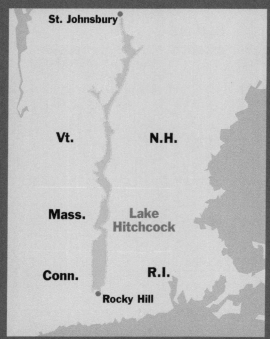

such glacier began to melt back from the Northeast about 21,500 years ago.

However, a mass of glacial deposits, mainly gravel and sand, in Rocky Hill, Conn., created a dam across the valley that prevented the historic river from reestablishing itself and emptying into Long Island Sound. Lake Hitchcock, which backed up behind the dam, was the result.

The legacy of Lake Hitchcock is the valley landscape today. The lake may have lasted from 16,000 to 12,000 years ago, when the Rocky Hill dam and other deposits that kept it in place failed. But over those 40 or so centuries, layers and layers of clay settled on the lake bottom, filling in the valley. Soil from dead vegetation built up atop the clay. And because the clay holds water, the soil holds water, making it some of the richest and most fertile farmland on the continent.

Stone walls, legacy of the ice age

Anyone who has hiked in remote areas of New England knows that miles of stone walls can run through the most isolated meadows and primitive forests. It's an astonishing mystery if you don't know the explanation. Who could have sweated and toiled to construct lines of carefully stacked rocks running from nowhere to nowhere? The answer is: the region's earliest European farmers.

Much of New England was once covered with farm fields, but many of those farms were abandoned in the years after the American Civil War, and the fields have since grown back to forests. But when early European farmers went to clear their land to plant crops, what they found were rocks and boulders, the debris dropped by New England's last glacier as it melted away.

So the region's stone walls were permanent fences around fields, but they were also trash piles for all those rocks and boulders.

In 1871, the U.S. Department of Agriculture decided to find out how many miles of fences, stone and otherwise,

Stone wall in Heath

there were in the nation. The study found there were more miles of stone walls in the Northeast then than there are miles of railroad tracks in the entire country today. In Massachusetts alone there were nearly 33,000 miles of stone walls.

The golden age for the building of stone walls in the region was probably from about 1775 to 1825, chiefly because that is the era when available wood for fencing was running out. The clearing of land for farming had deforested most of the state and much of the rest of New England. In addition, the Revolutionary War created a great need for wood fuel, and wood fence rails and many trees were used for that purpose.

Interestingly, within the Connecticut River Valley, there are distinct boundary lines defining where you will find stone walls and stone-filled soils and where you will not. Within the borders of old Lake Hitchcock, where mud and silt were laid down on the lake floor for centuries, the ice age deposit of rocks and debris has been covered up. As a result, the farms within these boundaries have been blessed with not only rich soils but largely stone-free soils as well.

Fitzgerald Lake in Florence in the old lakebed of Lake Hitchcock

The first Americans may have been a small band of hunters traveling in search of caribou or woolly mammoths more than 13,000 years ago who had no idea of the history they were about to make.

During the last ice age, so much of the Earth's water was ice that the surface of the ocean may have been more than 300 feet lower than it is today. As a result, a temporary land bridge emerged connecting Asia to Alaska. Human beings had already spread through much of Europe, Africa and Asia, but North America may still have been uninhabited by people.

The earliest North Americans may have entered Alaska from 17,000 to 40,000 years ago, but found their way south blocked by massive glaciers. However, it's believed that about 14,000 to 16,000 years ago, the climate warmed enough that a passage opened in the ice sheets allowing them to travel

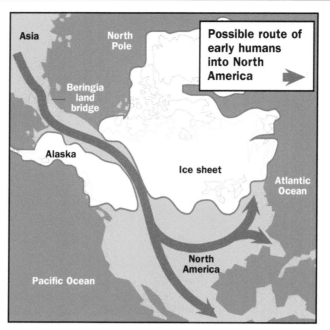

south into what is today the American Northwest. Others believe they may have bypassed the glaciers by traveling down the West Coast in boats much earlier.

Nevertheless, living for so long in frozen conditions, they may have been startled as they continued to travel south and east and began to encounter warmer temperatures and the vast forests and fields of America's heartland.

Archaeologists are detectives, piecing together clues about ancient people from the things they left behind. Occasionally, they find tools, artwork, trash or the remains of the buildings of the earliest residents of the Northeast. However, these artifacts have often been scattered, broken or changed through the centuries, making it difficult to determine what the earliest people in the region were like or how they lived.

In the 1920s, stone arrowheads were found near Clovis,

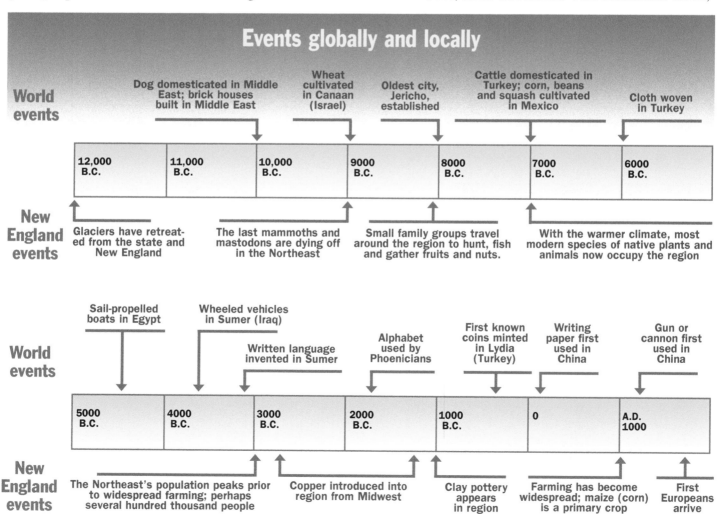

Events globally and locally

World events

| Dog domesticated in Middle East; brick houses built in Middle East | | Wheat cultivated in Canaan (Israel) | Oldest city, Jericho, established | Cattle domesticated in Turkey; corn, beans and squash cultivated in Mexico | | Cloth woven in Turkey |

| 12,000 B.C. | 11,000 B.C. | 10,000 B.C. | 9000 B.C. | 8000 B.C. | 7000 B.C. | 6000 B.C. |

New England events

| Glaciers have retreated from the state and New England | | The last mammoths and mastodons are dying off in the Northeast | Small family groups travel around the region to hunt, fish and gather fruits and nuts. | | With the warmer climate, most modern species of native plants and animals now occupy the region |

World events

| Sail-propelled boats in Egypt | Wheeled vehicles in Sumer (Iraq) | Written language invented in Sumer | Alphabet used by Phoenicians | First known coins minted in Lydia (Turkey) | Writing paper first used in China | Gun or cannon first used in China |

| 5000 B.C. | 4000 B.C. | 3000 B.C. | 2000 B.C. | 1000 B.C. | 0 | A.D. 1000 |

New England events

| The Northeast's population peaks prior to widespread farming; perhaps several hundred thousand people | Copper introduced into region from Midwest | | Clay pottery appears in region | Farming has become widespread; maize (corn) is a primary crop | First Europeans arrive |

First humans in Massachusetts

From the things that the earliest residents of New England left behind, archaeologists have been able to determine some things about their lives in the region.

From the stone tools and rock formations of campsites, as well as the charcoal remains of campfires that are sometimes found, they are able to guess what animals those who lived in the camps were hunting, what their living quarters were like and whether they lived in large or small communities. They are able to estimate how old the campsite is within a few hundred years by using a technique called radiocarbon dating to estimate the age of the charcoal.

Perhaps the earliest evidence of human beings in Massachusetts comes from a site in Ipswich, called Bull Brook, that is at least 10,400 years old. Knives, scrapers, drills and other tools as well as projectile points, beaver and caribou bones, and charcoal fragments have been found there. The site may have been an encampment for many families.

The Connecticut River likely drew many early humans. Artifacts dating to about the same period have been found in South Deerfield, Montague, Hampden and Chicopee.

New Mexico, that date back perhaps 13,000 years. For many years, the Clovis date was accepted as the earliest date for humans in North America. However, evidence was discovered in the 1970s for a human presence in Pennsylvania that may be earlier than the Clovis dates.

The Meadowcroft Rockshelter is a shallow cave overlooking a creek in southwestern Pennsylvania. Radiocarbon dating, which is a method for measuring the age of carbon in things like charcoal and other once-living material, found that the site may have been used by humans 16,000 years ago and possibly as early as 19,000 years ago. However, not all archaeologists accept these earlier dates, believing the radiocarbon readings may be flawed.

Adding to the controversy is that sites that also have pre-Clovis dates have been found in other locations, including Virginia, Oregon, South Carolina and Texas as well as South America. So the question of when humans first reached the Americas is not settled.

Nevertheless, the first arrivals in North America, whom we now call "paleoindians," which means the oldest Indians, probably had lives some people today would envy. After all, many may have had a wealth of food, land to live on and leisure time.

Were they savages? Not at all, say anthropologists. They were just as intelligent and inventive as people today. Human beings have probably been thinking at our modern level of complexity for the past 50,000 years. That means there was just as much genius among these early people as there is among modern humans. There was also just as much greed, charity, cruelty and compassion then as now.

It's true that life for humans has changed dramatically over the centuries as inventions and discoveries have accumulated. But humans' basic emotional and intellectual makeup has changed

very little. If these early human cultures did not advance much beyond the use of simple tools, it's because there was little need for them to advance. By many standards, they were "rich" people. Their needs could be easily met.

Indeed, they may have enjoyed life as much as many people today.

Paleoindians were a people frequently on the move, following the migration paths of the herd animals, such as caribou, or the waterfowl, such as ducks and geese, that they hunted. They also fished and trapped small game animals, such as beavers and rabbits, and they gathered and ate fruits, berries, nuts and some plants. In fact, plant matter may have made up much of their diet.

They probably carried their limited belongings on sleds or toboggans drawn by domesticated dogs or pulled by members of the group. Their tools included hammers, chisels, axes and awls (hole makers) made from rock, as well as other implements, such as sewing needles, made from bones or the ivory of mammoth tusks.

The sewing needle dates back at least 40,000 years. So the first Americans probably wore tailored clothes of furs and skins. And they probably lived in tents made of skins that had been loosely sewn together.

They would camp, possibly for weeks or months at a time, near where animals were known to seek food or water, for instance by a river, near a forest opening or around ponds or marshes. They would eventually move on, but if the hunting, fishing and berry picking were good enough, they might return to the same spot the next season.

The earliest residents of the Northeast probably had rich spiritual and social lives. Studies of modern-day hunting and gathering societies, such as those discovered in tropical rain forests, show they can be masters of conversation. Without tele-

Fishing line

Hooks were made of bone, and lines were weighted with a rock

vision and books, talk is their main source of entertainment and information.

They also relied on speech to pass along the knowledge accumulated over thousands of years – effective herbal cures, tips for hunting game, and designs of tents or layouts of camps.

It is likely they passed their leisure time doing craftwork, playing with wooden toys or games, singing and dancing, and just absorbing the beautiful scenery.

As the number of people grew in a region, it is also likely that many families came together at certain times of the year for festivals where goods were traded, stories swapped and marriages arranged.

Certainly, medicine was not as advanced as it is today. But the simplicity of that era offered its own protection. The level of stress for many paleoindians was probably very low. With so much food and land, war was not yet common, although personal arguments and hostilities have always existed.

While more babies died in infancy than die today, those who survived childhood could often live into their forties or fifties. Native Americans did not suffer many of the medical problems that are now widespread, such as obesity, diabetes and high blood pressure, which often result from inactive lives and diets high in fat.

Indeed, when the first Europeans arrived in America, they were struck by the great health Native Americans seemed to enjoy.

Ax
About 7 in. long; made perhaps 7,000 years ago.

What was life like for the Native Americans of the Northeast? For the centuries before Europeans settled widely in the region, life was simple in many respects and it was cyclical. It had the seasons as its clock.

Many Native American families would live by the seashore or a riverbank in summer, to fish and to gather food in nearby fields and forests. In winter, those by the coast might move to protected inland areas to hunt squirrels, beavers, deer, moose or bears and to live off stored supplies of vegetables, nuts and berries.

Farming became common in the Northeast about 1,000 years ago. Crops included maize (corn), beans, squash, pumpkins, cucumbers and tobacco. Villages often sat beside the agricultural fields. And a protective fence might be built around the edge of the village so that it could be a winter home or a fort.

To create open spaces for farming and for foot paths, Native Americans of the Northeast might periodically burn over the land, destroying the underbrush and many of the trees. The practice would also create more open land for hunting, and it would kill off insect pests near villages.

Crafting points for tools and weapons

Native Americans hunted game animals with spears and arrows and cleaned them with knives. The points on these tools and weapons were often made from rock called chert or flint. When chert was tapped with a sharp rock or other hard tool, flat flakes would come loose, allowing the rock to be fashioned into the desired shape.

Paleoindians would chisel grooves, called flutes, into the sides of the points so that once the point was finished, it might be tightly inserted into a notch in a stick. It was then tied into place with animal tendons, leather strips or other stringy material.

Points were sometimes made from other types of rock, including obsidian and quartzite.

Spear point
Made 5,000 to 6,000 years ago

Arrowhead
Made 500 to 2,000 years ago

Knife point
Made 5,000 to 7,000 years ago

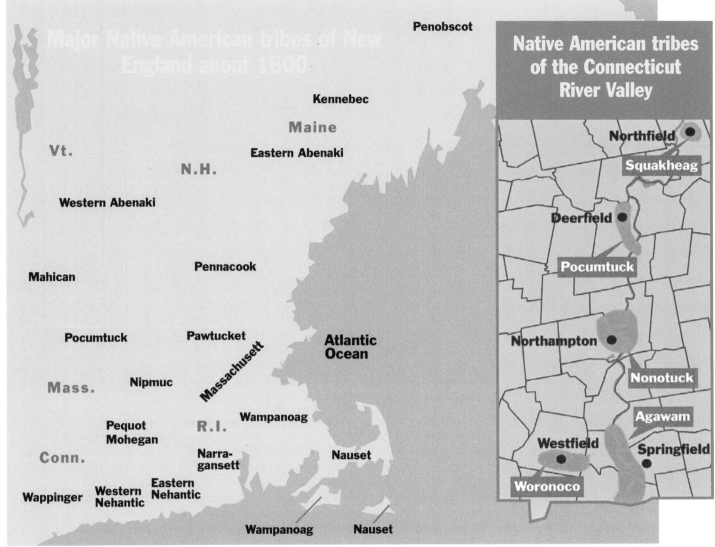

Major Native American tribes of New England about 1600

Penobscot

Kennebec

Maine

Eastern Abenaki

Vt.

N.H.

Western Abenaki

Mahican

Pennacook

Pocumtuck

Pawtucket

Atlantic Ocean

Massachusett

Mass.

Nipmuc

Pequot Mohegan

R.I.

Wampanoag

Nauset

Conn.

Narra-gansett

Wappinger

Western Nehantic

Eastern Nehantic

Wampanoag   Nauset

Native American tribes of the Connecticut River Valley

Northfield

Squakheag

Deerfield

Pocumtuck

Northampton

Nonotuck

Agawam

Westfield

Springfield

Woronoco

Throughout the Northeast, Native American women were responsible for raising children, preparing meals and tending the crops and the home. Men were hunters, warriors and craftsmen, making the tools, utensils and weapons needed for survival.

Native American children, especially boys, were encouraged at a young age to be bold and self-reliant. To prove he had reached manhood, a young male might be led blindfolded into the woods in winter, armed with a bow and arrow, a knife and a hatchet, and be expected to survive on his own until spring.

The most common clothing for both men and women in warm weather was the breech clout, a belt and cloth that performed the same function as a pair of shorts does today. In colder weather, sewn layers of animal skins might be worn, often of raccoon or fox, with the fur side of the skin against the body.

Wigwams or wetus

Bark or woven mats were laid over frames made of branches. A hole in the roof allowed smoke from fires to escape.

When the first Europeans arrived in the region in the early 1600s, there may have been several hundred thousand Native Americans living in the Northeast.

However, diseases contracted from the earliest European trappers and traders – smallpox, measles, influenza, typhoid fever and tuberculosis – killed many Native Americans. They had no history of these new illnesses and little or no immunity to them.

The first epidemic of the European illnesses, believed to include smallpox, probably began in the early 1600s. By 1700, up to 90 percent of the Native Americans in some areas of the Northeast had died from the diseases.

Because of disease and wars with Europeans, by 1800 the Native American way of life, which had defined how humans lived in the region for nearly 100 centuries, had disappeared from much of the Northeast.

The summit of Mount Greylock in North Adams

Some of the world's most magnificent mountains were once found in New England. But that was hundreds of millions of years ago. All those years of rain and wind, and the freeze and thaw of water in their crevices, have steadily eroded these peaks. Today, New England's mountains are minor when compared with mountains in other parts of the world.

There are 30 states with mountains that rise higher above sea level than the tallest in Massachusetts, Mount Greylock in Adams. And Mount Greylock, at 3,491 feet above sea level, is less than an eighth the height of the world's tallest mountain, Mount Everest. The highest peak in New England, at 6,289 feet, is Mount Washington in New Hampshire.

In the overall time scheme of Earth, mountains can disappear in a flash. With an erosion rate of just a millimeter a year (.04 inches), even a very tall mountain can be reduced to almost nothing over a few million years.

Within the Connecticut River Valley, the peaks so visible as one drives Interstate 91 – Mount Tom, Mount Holyoke and Mount Sugarloaf – can be counted on to last as scenery not too many more millions of years before they too will be reduced to little more than flat plains.

Mount Tom and Mount Holyoke began life as a flow of lava about 200 million years ago. Eventually the lava hardened into a broad flat plain of tough rock called basalt. Then, at some point, the entire lava field tipped up at about a 15-degree angle as the valley landscape settled. The Holyoke Range is the edge of the tipped lava field.

Mount Sugarloaf in Deerfield never pushed up in the conventional way mountains do. Everything around it just fell away. Mount Sugarloaf began life as part of a layer of

rock called conglomerate, which is a mixture of bits of many kinds of rock. But the conglomerate proved to be tougher than the rock around it. Eventually erosion wore down this surrounding rock, leaving the mountain as a highly visible feature in the valley.

Like people, mountains have a finite life – a vital youth, a stable middle age, then an old age where the ravages of time, via the erosion process, take their toll. The Himalayas are young mountains, still in their growth years, but the Berkshires and those in the Connecticut River Valley are old mountains where erosion is the most prominent natural force at work on them.

Erosion happens for more than one reason. Wind and rain are usually the primary tools for wearing rocks down. But rocks also erode because water can get into their crevices, freeze in winter and then expand, cracking the rock. In addition, plant roots can penetrate crevices, spreading them further and eventually cracking the underlying rock. The chemicals released by decaying plants also speed erosion.

Generally, the taller the mountain is, the higher the erosion rate. For one thing, the climate at a higher altitude is usually harsher. But the key is not the elevation; it is the slope. And higher mountain peaks usually have steeper slopes. Water loaded with sediments will run down a steep slope faster, wearing away the rock beneath it.

Erosion is by no means a steady process. A landslide may remove a huge chunk of a mountain in a day, lowering a peak by dozens of feet. But over a million years, even with the occasional landslide, the erosion rate may average only a fraction of an inch each year. In addition, the erosion rate is typically higher when a mountain is

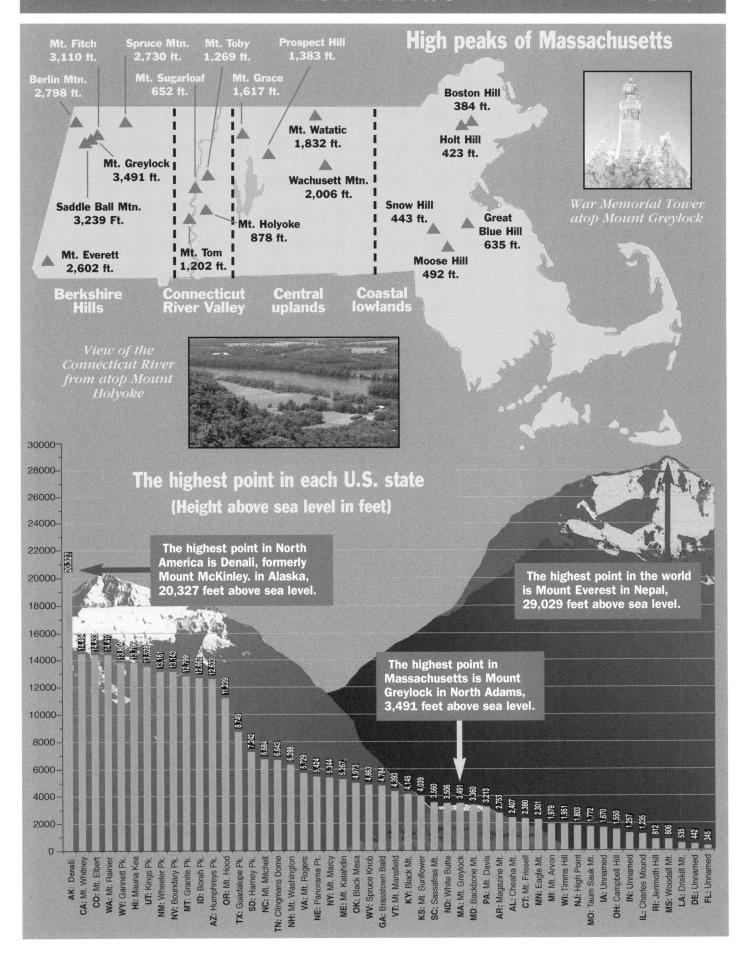

High peaks of Massachusetts

Mt. Fitch 3,110 ft.
Berlin Mtn. 2,798 ft.
Spruce Mtn. 2,730 ft.
Mt. Sugarloaf 652 ft.
Mt. Toby 1,269 ft.
Mt. Grace 1,617 ft.
Prospect Hill 1,383 ft.
Mt. Greylock 3,491 ft.
Saddle Ball Mtn. 3,239 Ft.
Mt. Everett 2,602 ft.
Mt. Tom 1,202 ft.
Mt. Holyoke 878 ft.
Mt. Watatic 1,832 ft.
Wachusett Mtn. 2,006 ft.
Boston Hill 384 ft.
Holt Hill 423 ft.
Snow Hill 443 ft.
Great Blue Hill 635 ft.
Moose Hill 492 ft.

Berkshire Hills
Connecticut River Valley
Central uplands
Coastal lowlands

War Memorial Tower atop Mount Greylock

View of the Connecticut River from atop Mount Holyoke

The highest point in each U.S. state
(Height above sea level in feet)

The highest point in North America is Denali, formerly Mount McKinley. in Alaska, 20,327 feet above sea level.

The highest point in the world is Mount Everest in Nepal, 29,029 feet above sea level.

The highest point in Massachusetts is Mount Greylock in North Adams, 3,491 feet above sea level.

State	Height
AK: Denali	20,327
CA: Mt. Whitney	14,494
CO: Mt. Elbert	14,433
WA: Mt. Rainier	14,410
WY: Gannett Pk.	13,804
HI: Mauna Kea	13,796
UT: Kings Pk.	13,528
NM: Wheeler Pk.	13,161
NV: Boundary Pk.	13,143
MT: Granite Pk.	12,799
ID: Borah Pk.	12,662
AZ: Humphreys Pk.	12,633
OR: Mt. Hood	11,239
TX: Guadalupe Pk.	8,749
SD: Harney Pk.	7,242
NC: Mt. Mitchell	6,684
TN: Clingmans Dome	6,643
NH: Mt. Washington	6,288
VA: Mt. Rogers	5,729
NE: Panorama Pt.	5,424
NY: Mt. Marcy	5,344
ME: Mt. Katahdin	5,267
OK: Black Mesa	4,973
WV: Spruce Knob	4,863
GA: Brasstown Bald	4,784
VT: Mt. Mansfield	4,393
KY: Black Mt.	4,145
KS: Mt. Sunflower	4,039
SC: Sassafras Mt.	3,560
ND: White Butte	3,506
MA: Mt. Greylock	3,491
MD: Backbone Mt.	3,360
PA: Mt. Davis	3,213
AR: Magazine Mt.	2,753
AL: Cheaha Mt.	2,407
CT: Mt. Frissell	2,380
MN: Eagle Mt.	2,301
MI: Mt. Arvon	1,979
WI: Timms Hill	1,951
NJ: High Point	1,803
MO: Taum Sauk Mt.	1,772
IA: Unnamed	1,670
OH: Campbell Hill	1,550
IN: Unnamed	1,257
IL: Charles Mound	1,235
RI: Jerimoth Hill	812
MS: Woodall Mt.	806
LA: Driskill Mt.	535
DE: Unnamed	442
FL: Unnamed	345

Mount Sugarloaf in South Deerfield

young than when it is old.

How fast are all these mountains, from Everest to Sugarloaf, eroding? Erosion rates vary. The rate that the Himalayas are flattening is among the highest in the world. While no one knows for sure what it is, many believe that for Mount Everest, the highest peak in the world at 29,029 feet above sea level, the rate over the last million or so years has been about a centimeter (.4 inches) a year. Interestingly, the rate at which the peak is falling from erosion may be about the rate at which it is still rising, leaving the overall height of Everest stable.

The erosion rate for Mount Greylock is probably similar to that of other older mountain peaks in the Appalachians. One study in the Great Smoky Mountains estimated the rate there to be about .03 millimeters per year. That translates to erosion over a million years of about 100 feet.

For the peaks in this region along the Connecticut River, erosion rates may be very low. Mount Tom, at 1,202 feet above sea level, and Mount Holyoke, at 878 feet above sea level, are made up of very tough, hardened lava, which is resistant to erosion. Mount Sugarloaf, at 652 feet above sea level at the visitor's center on its peak, is made up of a particularly tough conglomerate.

The best evidence for just how little erosion is going on atop those peaks is visible to the naked eye. Some 30,000 years ago, during the last ice age, a glacier more than a mile high covered Western Massachusetts, even its mountains, and as it flowed over the landscape, rocks embedded in its lowest layer scraped over the bedrock of mountain peaks, leaving characteristic scratches. If you hike to the top of Mount Holyoke, you can still see the scratches. That means there has been very little erosion on the mountain's top surface in all those years. The same kind of scratches can be seen atop Mount Sugarloaf.

The Appalachian National Scenic Trail

Usually called just the Appalachian Trail, it extends from Springer Mountain in Georgia to Mount Katahdin in Maine, traveling about 2,200 miles through 14 states, including Massachusetts. The first section opened in 1923 in New York. The trail is maintained by various trail clubs and private landowners along the way, and it is managed by the National Park Service and the Appalachian Trail Conservancy.

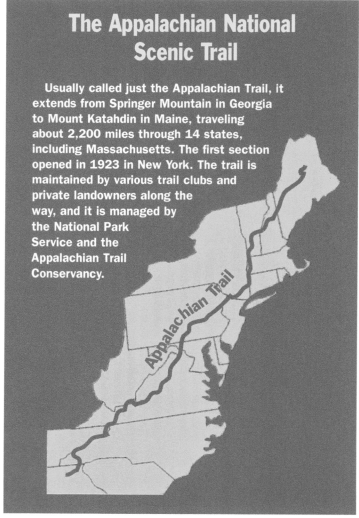

View from Monument Mountain in Great Barrington

You never have to travel far in Massachusetts to find water. With more than 2,000 rivers and streams as well as nearly 3,000 lakes and ponds, not to mention the Atlantic Ocean on its coast, Massachusetts has water, water everywhere – and quite a lot to drink.

Most people think of the Pacific Northwest as America's rain capital. In fact, Seattle gets less precipitation each year (an average of 38.8 inches) than Springfield (about 42 inches).

The presence of so much water gives the state a great diversity of wildlife. There is a long list of plants and animals that live only in water and another long list of wildlife that live alongside water.

The land surface of Massachusetts slopes from the Berkshire Hills on the west to the Atlantic Coast on the east. It also slopes toward Long Island Sound on the south. These gradual slopes have produced one group of rivers that flow generally east, such as the Deerfield and Westfield rivers, and another set that flows generally south, such as the Connecticut River.

A half century ago, many of the state's major rivers were polluted eyesores because of the sewage, chemicals and trash that were being dumped into them. The Connecticut River was described as the nation's "best landscaped sewer" in the 1950s. However, with the passage of the federal Clean Water Act in 1972, and with citizen and government action to clean up the state's waterways, many, including the Connecticut River, became clean enough that today they are recreational attractions instead of places to be avoided.

Most Western Massachusetts cities and towns get their water from municipal reservoirs or from wells that tap underground lakes of water, called aquifers, places where water collects beneath the surface but doesn't drain away.

Connecticut River at Springfield

Lake or pond?

The usual definition of a pond is that it is shallow enough for aquatic plants to grow anywhere in it. But a lake can be so deep and dark in places that plants only grow in the shallow areas.

Wetlands

Between dry land and the deep water of lakes, rivers or the ocean, you will often see wetlands, areas where land and water mix, such as swamps, marshes, bogs, wet meadows and riverbank forests that may flood after heavy rains.

Wetlands were once considered places of no value in much of America, and in the last two centuries more than half the acreage of wetlands in the lower 48 states has been filled, drained or otherwise lost.

But wetlands do have great value, people have learned. They filter out pollution before it reaches larger bodies of water, and they are home to many kinds of plants and animals, from cattails to muskrats, that are seen almost nowhere else. That's why wetlands are now protected by law.

Since 1780 in Massachusetts, nearly 28 percent of the state's wetlands have disappeared, most of them inland freshwater wetlands. The state now has about half a million acres of freshwater and saltwater wetlands.

Lily pads

Its Native American name was "Quinnetuket," the long river. The Connecticut River travels 410 miles from its headwaters near the Canadian border to its mouth on Long Island Sound.

The longest river in New England, it flows through four states: Vermont and New Hampshire, forming the common border between them, as well as through Massachusetts and Connecticut. In Massachusetts, it touches on 19 communities, has an average current of about five miles per hour, an average depth of 10 to 15 feet, and an average width of 1,200 feet, a bit less than a quarter of a mile.

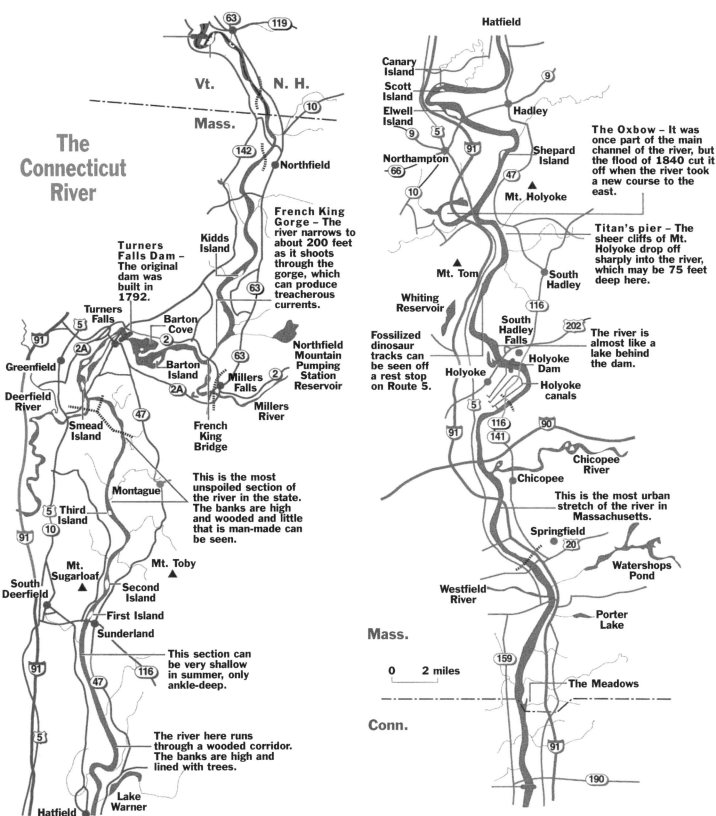

The Connecticut River

Turners Falls Dam – The original dam was built in 1792.

French King Gorge – The river narrows to about 200 feet as it shoots through the gorge, which can produce treacherous currents.

This is the most unspoiled section of the river in the state. The banks are high and wooded and little that is man-made can be seen.

This section can be very shallow in summer, only ankle-deep.

The river here runs through a wooded corridor. The banks are high and lined with trees.

The Oxbow – It was once part of the main channel of the river, but the flood of 1840 cut it off when the river took a new course to the east.

Titan's pier – The sheer cliffs of Mt. Holyoke drop off sharply into the river, which may be 75 feet deep here.

The river is almost like a lake behind the dam.

Fossilized dinosaur tracks can be seen off a rest stop on Route 5.

This is the most urban stretch of the river in Massachusetts.

0   2 miles

Rivers

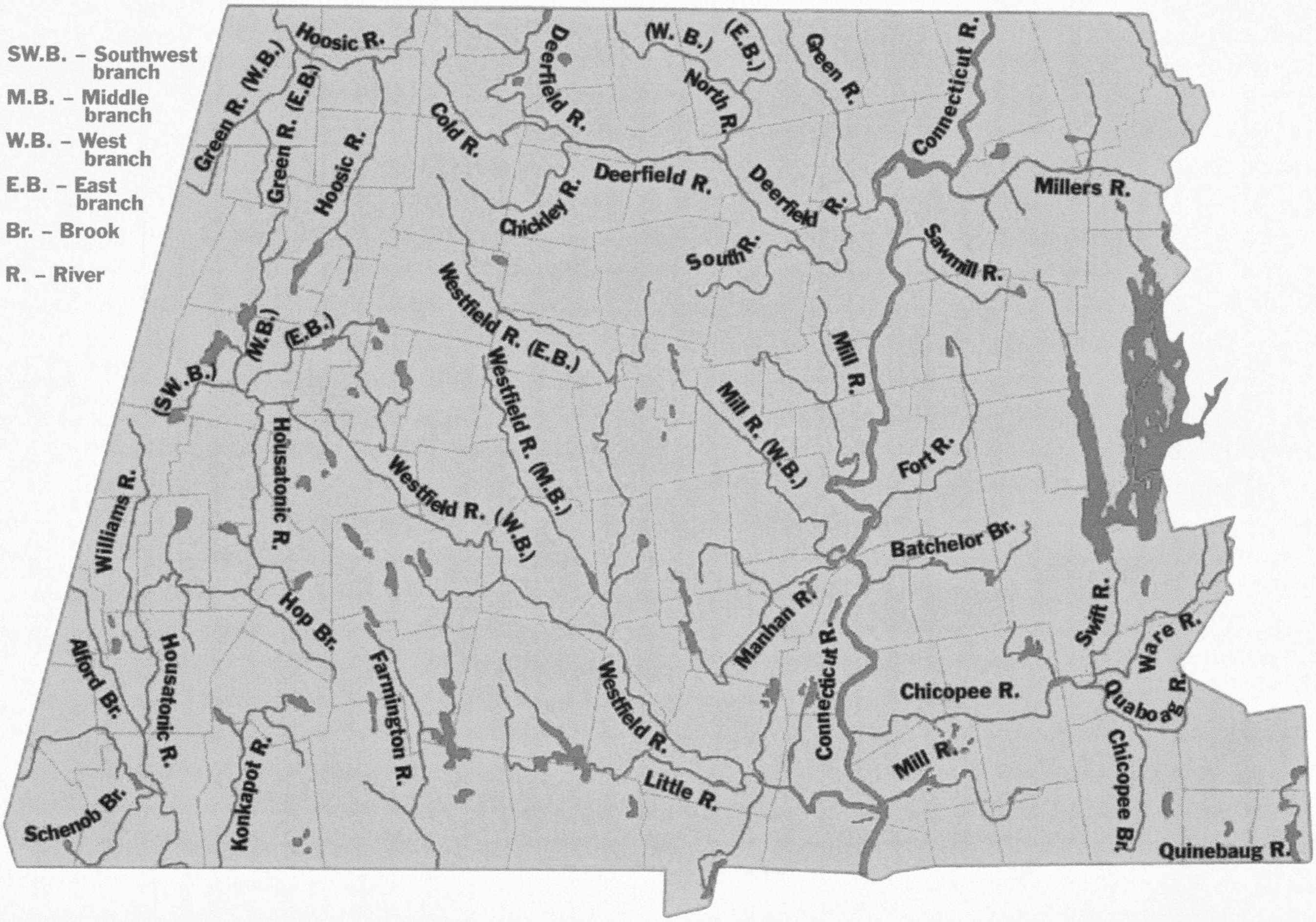

SW.B. – Southwest branch
M.B. – Middle branch
W.B. – West branch
E.B. – East branch
Br. – Brook
R. – River

(Map of rivers with labels: Hoosic R., Green R. (W.B.), Green R. (E.B.), Hoosic R., Deerfield R., (W.B.), (E.B.), North R., Green R., Connecticut R., Cold R., Chickley R., Deerfield R., Deerfield R., Millers R., South R., Sawmill R., Westfield R. (E.B.), W.B., E.B., S.W.B., Westfield R. (M.B.), Mill R., Mill R. (W.B.), Fort R., Housatonic R., Westfield R. (W.B.), Batchelor Br., Williams R., Hop Br., Farmington R., Westfield R., Manhan R., Swift R., Ware R., Chicopee R., Alford Br., Housatonic R., Konkapot R., Little R., Connecticut R., Mill R., Quaboag R., Chicopee Br., Schenob Br., Quinebaug R.)

Chicopee River
Length: 18 miles
Source: Marshes at the headwaters of the Swift, Ware and Quaboag rivers
Mouth: Connecticut River

Connecticut River
Length: 410 miles
Source: Waters near the Canadian border
Mouth: Long Island Sound

Deerfield River
Length: 76 miles
Source: Vermont waters
Mouth: Connecticut River

Farmington River
Length: 80 miles
Source: Brooks in Becket
Mouth: Connecticut River

The Connecticut River as seen from Mount Sugarloaf in South Deerfield

Hoosic River
Length: 76 miles
Source: Above Cheshire Reservoir
Mouth: Hudson River

Housatonic River
Length: 149 miles
Source: Three water bodies in Central Berkshire County
Mouth: Long Island Sound

Millers River
Length: 52 miles
Source: Waters in N. H. and North Central Mass.
Mouth: Connecticut River

Westfield River
Length: 62.5 miles (E.B.)
Source: Brooks in Savoy
Mouth: Connecticut River

Lakes, ponds and reservoirs

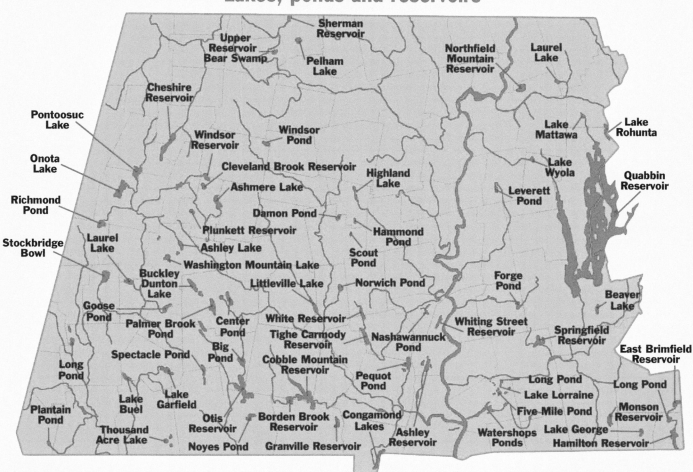

Sherman Reservoir
Upper Reservoir Bear Swamp
Pelham Lake
Northfield Mountain Reservoir
Laurel Lake
Cheshire Reservoir
Pontoosuc Lake
Lake Mattawa
Lake Rohunta
Windsor Reservoir
Windsor Pond
Onota Lake
Cleveland Brook Reservoir
Highland Lake
Lake Wyola
Quabbin Reservoir
Ashmere Lake
Richmond Pond
Leverett Pond
Damon Pond
Stockbridge Bowl
Plunkett Reservoir
Hammond Pond
Laurel Lake
Ashley Lake
Scout Pond
Washington Mountain Lake
Buckley Dunton Lake
Littleville Lake
Norwich Pond
Forge Pond
Goose Pond
Beaver Lake
Palmer Brook Pond
Center Pond
White Reservoir
Whiting Street Reservoir
Springfield Reservoir
Spectacle Pond
Big Pond
Tighe Carmody Reservoir
Nashawannuck Pond
East Brimfield Reservoir
Long Pond
Cobble Mountain Reservoir
Pequot Pond
Long Pond
Long Pond
Lake Buel
Lake Garfield
Lake Lorraine
Plantain Pond
Otis Reservoir
Borden Brook Reservoir
Congamond Lakes
Five-Mile Pond
Monson Reservoir
Thousand Acre Lake
Noyes Pond
Granville Reservoir
Ashley Reservoir
Watershops Ponds
Lake George
Hamilton Reservoir

Quabbin Reservoir

On April 27, 1938, the crowd that gathered in the Enfield Town Hall listened to McEnelly's Orchestra play "Home Sweet Home." Then the music in Enfield died forever. The town ceased to exist.

Enfield, Dana, Greenwich and Prescott would soon be flooded to create what was then the world's largest man-made source of water, Quabbin Reservoir, to serve as the main water supply for Boston and much of eastern Massachusetts.

Nearly 2,500 people would lose their homes so that the reservoir could be created. And for many of them, the last moments of their towns were tearful ones. The "Farewell Ball" at the Enfield Town Hall drew an overflow crowd. At midnight, the four towns were to officially lose their incorporation. One newspaper account described the scene as the clock struck the fateful hour:

"A hush fell over the Town Hall, jammed far beyond ordinary capacity, as the first note of the clock sounded; a nervous tension ... has been felt by both present and former residents and casual onlookers ... muffled sounds of sobbing were heard, hardened men were not ashamed to take out their handkerchiefs and even children attending the ball with their parents broke into tears."

The actual flooding of the valley began in 1939 using water from the Ware and Swift rivers, but it was not until 1946 that the wide valley was finally full. Quabbin Reservoir covers 39 square miles, it has a shoreline of 118 miles and, when it is full, it holds 412 billion gallons.

Quabbin Reservoir as viewed from the observation tower, above right

Western Massachusetts waterfalls

It's the contrast that's striking – as if you've stumbled upon a three-ring circus in the middle of a desert.

Hiking through a forest, with the silence broken only by the occasional birdsong, one may gradually be aware of a vague roar of water ahead. Fifty yards more and it may turn eerily loud, totally out of place in such a quiet landscape. Waterfalls precede themselves that way.

Waterfalls fall into categories. A cascade is a waterfall that typically descends gradually, in a series of small steps. It may be just a brook or stream moving down a slope of rocks. A cataract is a waterfall with a single, sheer drop that usually involves a large volume of water. What aren't cataracts or cascades fall back into the general category of waterfalls.

Waterfalls are usually found where there is a considerable rise and fall to the land and where there is rain. Western Massachusetts has the type of topography that is favorable to their formation. And it certainly has rain, from 40 to 45 inches of precipitation a year in most locations.

Classic waterfalls, like Niagara Falls in New York, are usually found in places where hard rock meets softer rock. When water flows over the two, the softer rock erodes quickly and the hard rock does not, creating a sudden drop.

Salmon Falls in Shelburne Falls

Bash Bish Falls in Mount Washington

1 Pauchaug Falls
2 Old Wendell Road Falls
3 Four Mile Brook Falls
4 Briggs Brook Falls
5 Bear's Den Falls
6 Buffam Falls
7 Roaring Brook Falls
8 Slatestone Brook Falls
9 Gunn Brook Falls
10 Chapel Falls
11 Sluice Brook Falls
12 Salmon Falls

13 Twin Cascades
14 Tannery Falls
15 Peck Brook Falls
16 March Cataract Falls
17 Deer Hill Falls
18 Money Brook Falls
19 Wahconah Falls
20 Glendale Falls
21 Sanderson Brook Falls
22 Campbell Falls
23 Race Brook Falls
24 Bash Bish Falls

See page 4 for city and town names.

Slatestone Brook Falls in Sunderland

Normal daily temperature (F°)

January maximum
- 40°-45°
- 35°-40°
- 30°-35°
- 25°-30°
- 20°-25°

January minimum
- 25°-30°
- 20°-25°
- 15°-20°
- 10°-15°
- 5°-10°
- 0°-5°

July maximum
- 85°-90°
- 80°-85°
- 75°-80°
- 70°-75°

July minimum
- 65°-70°
- 60°-65°
- 55°-60°
- 50°-55°
- 45°-50°

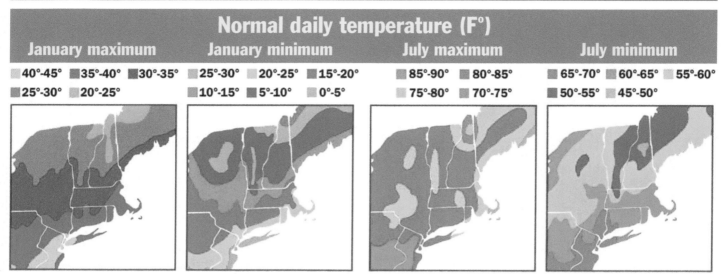

Local measurements may differ sharply depending on such things as elevation, position in relation to mountains or large water bodies, and the urbanization of the area.

Annual snowfall
- 12 - 24 in.
- 24 - 36 in.
- 36 - 60 in.
- 60 - 100 in.
- 100+ in.

Peak colors of fall foliage
- Sept. 20 - Oct. 1
- Sept. 25 - Oct. 5
- Oct. 1 - Oct. 12
- Oct. 3 - Oct. 15
- Oct. 5 - Oct. 18
- Oct. 12 - Oct. 25
- Oct. 15 - Oct. 29
- Oct. 23 - Nov. 5

Annual precipitation
- 24 - 32 in.
- 32 - 40 in.
- 40 - 48 in.
- 48 - 56 in.

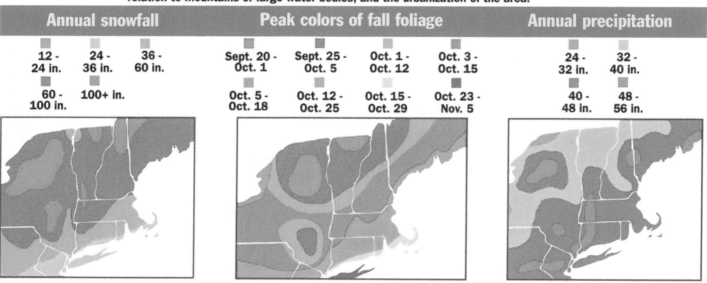

Sunrise and sunset in Western Massachusetts

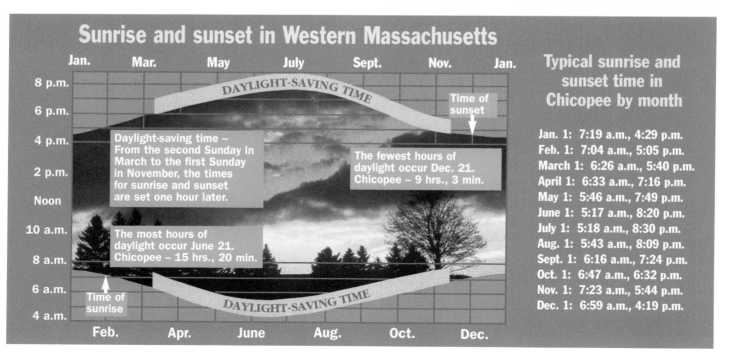

DAYLIGHT-SAVING TIME

Daylight-saving time – From the second Sunday in March to the first Sunday in November, the times for sunrise and sunset are set one hour later.

The fewest hours of daylight occur Dec. 21. Chicopee – 9 hrs., 3 min.

The most hours of daylight occur June 21. Chicopee – 15 hrs., 20 min.

Time of sunset / Time of sunrise

Typical sunrise and sunset time in Chicopee by month

Jan. 1: 7:19 a.m., 4:29 p.m.
Feb. 1: 7:04 a.m., 5:05 p.m.
March 1: 6:26 a.m., 5:40 p.m.
April 1: 6:33 a.m., 7:16 p.m.
May 1: 5:46 a.m., 7:49 p.m.
June 1: 5:17 a.m., 8:20 p.m.
July 1: 5:18 a.m., 8:30 p.m.
Aug. 1: 5:43 a.m., 8:09 p.m.
Sept. 1: 6:16 a.m., 7:24 p.m.
Oct. 1: 6:47 a.m., 6:32 p.m.
Nov. 1: 7:23 a.m., 5:44 p.m.
Dec. 1: 6:59 a.m., 4:19 p.m.

Weather in the hills and in the valley

Chicopee	Jan.	Feb.	Mar.	Apr.	May	June	July	Aug.	Sept.	Oct.	Nov.	Dec.	Total or annual avg.
Normal daily temp.	26	28	37	49	60	69	74	72	64	52	42	31	50
Precipitation (inches)	3.2	3.0	3.4	3.7	3.8	3.7	3.8	3.6	3.4	3.1	3.9	3.5	42.1
Snowfall (inches)	14	12	10	2	–	–	–	–	–	–	2	11	51

North Adams	Jan.	Feb.	Mar.	Apr.	May	June	July	Aug.	Sept.	Oct.	Nov.	Dec.	Total or annual avg.
Normal daily temp.	22	23	36	48	61	65	68	68	57	51	39	27	47
Precipitation (inches)	3.6	3.2	3.7	3.7	3.7	3.8	4.0	3.7	3.8	3.2	3.9	3.7	44.0
Snowfall (inches)	22	22	16	6	–	–	–	–	–	–	6	15	87

Record temperatures

Chicopee (since 1943):
102° on June 26, 1952;
–22° on Jan. 22, 1961

North Adams (since 1974):
97° on July 20, 1991
and July 14, 1995;
–29° on Jan. 27, 1994

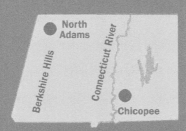

North Adams
Berkshire Hills
Connecticut River
Chicopee

Typical high and low temperatures in Chicopee by month

Jan. 1: 33°, 18°   July 1: 82°, 61°
Feb. 1: 32°, 15°   Aug. 1: 82°, 61°
March 1: 39°, 22°   Sept. 1: 79°, 57°
April 1: 51°, 34°   Oct. 1: 68°, 45°
May 1: 65°, 42°   Nov. 1: 58°, 37°
June 1: 75°, 52°   Dec. 1: 40°, 24°

Backyard signs of spring

Average timing for indicators of spring,
based on five years of observations in Northampton

First scent of skunk in the air
Feb. 17

First robin on the lawn
March 20

Green appearing in the grass
March 25

First dandelion on the lawn
April 20

First cabbage white butterfly
April 20

Buds breaking on sugar maples
April 25

The Great Blizzard of 1888

Considered the most severe snowstorm in New England's history, the Great Blizzard of 1888 began on March 11 and it continued to snow for a day and a half. Some 30 to 50 inches of snow fell on Western Massachusetts. In places, drifts stood 30 to 40 feet, covering whole houses.

Blizzard of 1888, Springfield

Snow and Cold
(Springfield statistics)

Average date of first snow since 1950: Nov. 25

Average date of first frost (32°) since 2005: Oct. 16

Average date of first hard frost (28°) since 2005: Oct. 24

Largest seasonal snowfall since 1950: 107.7 in., winter of 1995-96

Smallest seasonal snowfall since 1950: 16.1 in., winter of 1979-80

WESTERN MASSACHUSETTS NATURE CALENDAR

January

1	2	3	4	5	6	7
Brown trout eggs, laid in gravel-bottomed streams in fall, are slowly developing.			Red-spotted newts are active under the ice all winter.		Bullfrogs are settled in the mud at the bottom of ponds, waiting for the spring thaw.	

8	9	10	11	12	13	14
Trees are in a semi-dormant state, living off stored nutrients.			Many white-tailed deer lose their antlers in coming weeks and regrow them in the spring.		Watch for red-tailed hawks perched in roadside trees, searching for prey below.	

15	16	17	18	19	20	21
The coldest temperatures, strongest winds and heaviest snowfalls of the year may occur about now.			Eagles from the north will migrate into Massachusetts in winter to fish the open waters of Quabbin Reservoir and the Connecticut River.			

22	23	24	25	26	27	28
Female red foxes are establishing their dens, preparing to bear young later in the spring.			Raccoons, beavers and gray squirrels are entering their breeding seasons.		Black bear cubs are being born in winter dens.	

29	30	31				
On warm days this time of year, bluebottle flies may emerge in attics and in sunny unused rooms.						

February

1	2	3	4	5	6	7
Coyotes are breeding.	Great horned owls are beginning to nest, one of the first birds to do so each year.			On the south side of trees, look for snow fleas, which may resemble small black specks.		

8	9	10	11	12	13	14
Beneath the ice on frozen lakes and ponds, bluegills and sunfish are nearly dormant, but yellow perch, bass and trout are still active.				Skunks are venturing out to breed. Their scent is a sign spring is approaching.		

15	16	17	18	19	20	21
Ring-necked ducks begin migrating through the state as they fly north to nest in Maine and Canada.			The first killdeer of the season may show up on plowed fields if the ground is free of snow.		Maple sap begins to run about this time.	

22	23	24	25	26	27	28
Flocks of red-winged blackbirds and common grackles are returning from the south.			Cardinals and chickadees are beginning to sing their spring songs.		Turkey vultures are returning to the region.	

29						
Leap day occurs every fourth year.						

WESTERN MASSACHUSETTS NATURE CALENDAR

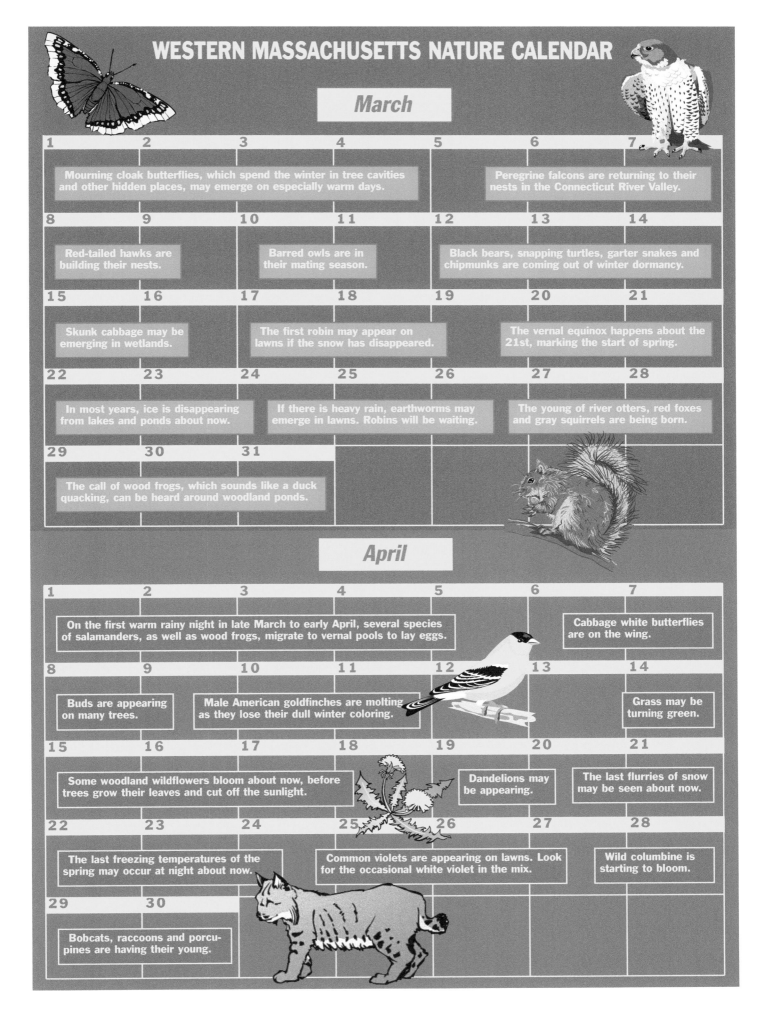

March

1	2	3	4	5	6	7
Mourning cloak butterflies, which spend the winter in tree cavities and other hidden places, may emerge on especially warm days.				Peregrine falcons are returning to their nests in the Connecticut River Valley.		

8	9	10	11	12	13	14
Red-tailed hawks are building their nests.		Barred owls are in their mating season.		Black bears, snapping turtles, garter snakes and chipmunks are coming out of winter dormancy.		

15	16	17	18	19	20	21
Skunk cabbage may be emerging in wetlands.		The first robin may appear on lawns if the snow has disappeared.		The vernal equinox happens about the 21st, marking the start of spring.		

22	23	24	25	26	27	28
In most years, ice is disappearing from lakes and ponds about now.		If there is heavy rain, earthworms may emerge in lawns. Robins will be waiting.		The young of river otters, red foxes and gray squirrels are being born.		

29	30	31
The call of wood frogs, which sounds like a duck quacking, can be heard around woodland ponds.		

April

1	2	3	4	5	6	7
On the first warm rainy night in late March to early April, several species of salamanders, as well as wood frogs, migrate to vernal pools to lay eggs.					Cabbage white butterflies are on the wing.	

8	9	10	11	12	13	14
Buds are appearing on many trees.		Male American goldfinches are molting as they lose their dull winter coloring.				Grass may be turning green.

15	16	17	18	19	20	21
Some woodland wildflowers bloom about now, before trees grow their leaves and cut off the sunlight.				Dandelions may be appearing.		The last flurries of snow may be seen about now.

22	23	24	25	26	27	28
The last freezing temperatures of the spring may occur at night about now.			Common violets are appearing on lawns. Look for the occasional white violet in the mix.			Wild columbine is starting to bloom.

29	30
Bobcats, raccoons and porcupines are having their young.	

WESTERN MASSACHUSETTS NATURE CALENDAR

May

1	2	3	4	5	6	7
Ruby-throated hummingbirds are returning from the south.		Snakes and turtles spend the day basking in the sun to warm their bodies.			The leaves on most trees have fully opened. Sugar maples will leaf out before red maples.	

8	9	10	11	12	13	14
Warblers have been arriving from the south in recent weeks.		Many songbirds, including robins, cardinals and chickadees, are laying eggs.		The young of mallards and other ducks are hatching. Within a day they will take to water.		

15	16	17	18	19	20	21
Jack-in-the-pulpits are blooming.		Many butterflies are out, including eastern black swallowtails and little wood satyrs.			Downy woodpeckers are laying their eggs in tree cavities.	

22	23	24	25	26	27	28
Wild lupines are flowering in meadows.		Wood turtles are laying eggs in areas of sand or gravel.			Violets are disappearing from lawns and fields.	

29	30	31				
Treefrogs are in their breeding season and are most likely to be seen this time of year.						

June

1	2	3	4	5	6	7
Monarch butterflies are returning to the region.			White-tailed deer are having their young.		June bugs are emerging, often swarming around porch lights.	

8	9	10	11	12	13	14
Painted and snapping turtles are climbing out of ponds to lay their eggs.				Fragrant water lilies are blooming in ponds and Queen Anne's lace is flowering along roadsides.		

15	16	17	18	19	20	21
Black-eyed Susans, oxeye daisies and other field wildflowers are coming into bloom.				Day lilies are blooming.	The summer solstice happens about the 21st, marking the start of summer.	

22	23	24	25	26	27	28
Snakes that lay eggs, such as milk snakes, are doing so about now. Other snakes, like garter snakes, have live young later in the season.					The flashing of fireflies can be seen at night above fields and meadows.	

29	30					
Bears are in the heart of their breeding season.						

WESTERN MASSACHUSETTS NATURE CALENDAR

July

1	2	3	4	5	6	7

The young of many raptors, such as red-tailed hawks and great horned owls, are fully grown and out on their own by now.

The season's second generation of clouded sulphur and spring azure butterflies is emerging.

8	9	10	11	12	13	14

Butter and eggs is in bloom along roadsides and in meadows.

Wild blueberries are ripening.

The greatest amount of sunshine and the least cloudiness during daylight hours occurs about this time of year.

15	16	17	18	19	20	21

Katydids and crickets can be heard calling at night.

The whine of cicadas can be heard during the heat of the day.

Tadpoles are emerging from green frog eggs.

22	23	24	25	26	27	28

The flutelike trill of gray treefrogs can be heard on cloudy days.

Chipmunks may be having their second litter of young this year.

The delicate orange flowers of jewelweed, also called touch-me-not, are in bloom.

29	30	31

The hottest days of summer may occur about now and into early August.

August

1	2	3	4	5	6	7

Goldfinches are beginning to nest, among the latest of any of the songbirds to do so.

With the breeding season for frogs over, ponds have become quiet.

Garter snakes may be having their young.

8	9	10	11	12	13	14

Grasshopper and yellow jacket populations are increasing.

Shooting stars from the annual Perseid meteor shower can be seen at night.

Great blue herons have abandoned their nests for the season.

15	16	17	18	19	20	21

Many types of goldenrod are blooming in fields and along roadsides. Joe-Pye weed is blooming around wetlands.

On rainy days, red-spotted newts can be seen on dirt roads in rural areas.

22	23	24	25	26	27	28

The season's third generation of cabbage white butterflies is emerging.

The final heat wave of the summer may occur about now.

Leopard frogs can sometimes be seen in back yards.

29	30	31

Tree swallows have moved to coastal areas, preparing to migrate.

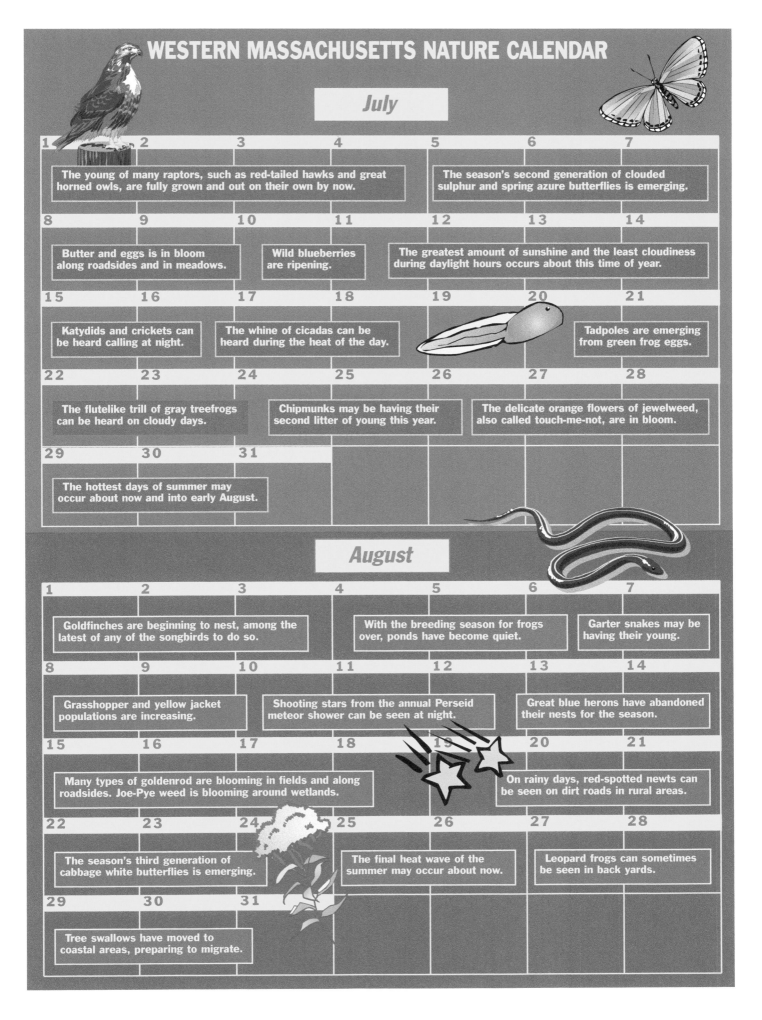

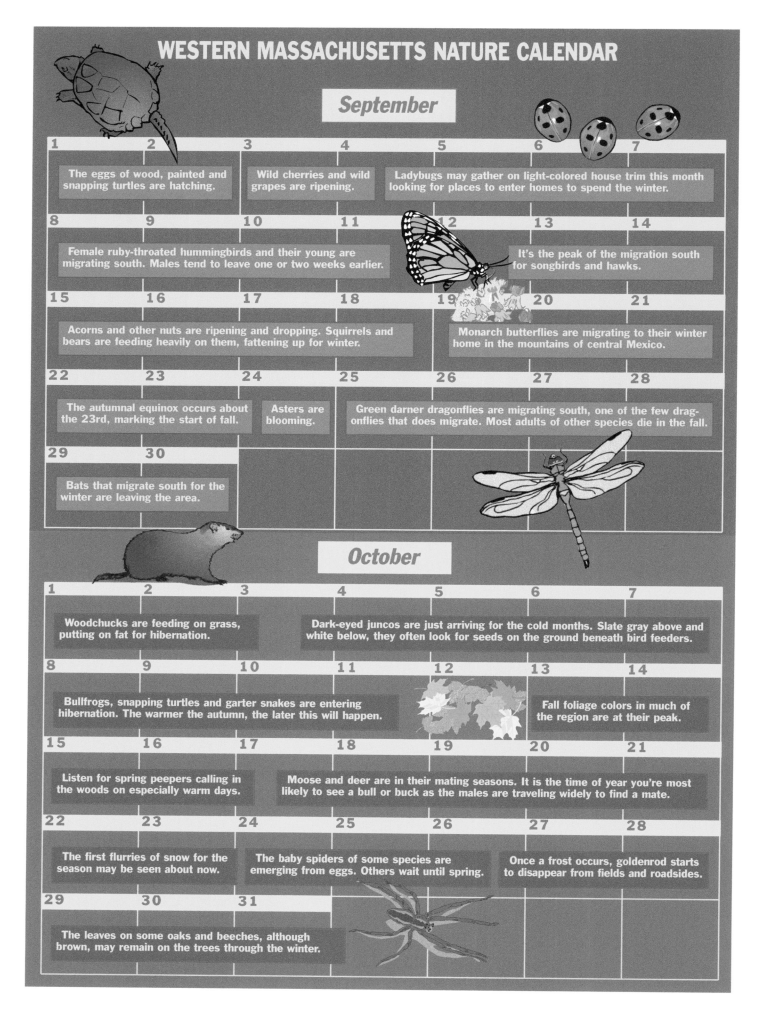

WESTERN MASSACHUSETTS NATURE CALENDAR

September

1 2 3 4 5 6 7

The eggs of wood, painted and snapping turtles are hatching.

Wild cherries and wild grapes are ripening.

Ladybugs may gather on light-colored house trim this month looking for places to enter homes to spend the winter.

8 9 10 11 12 13 14

Female ruby-throated hummingbirds and their young are migrating south. Males tend to leave one or two weeks earlier.

It's the peak of the migration south for songbirds and hawks.

15 16 17 18 19 20 21

Acorns and other nuts are ripening and dropping. Squirrels and bears are feeding heavily on them, fattening up for winter.

Monarch butterflies are migrating to their winter home in the mountains of central Mexico.

22 23 24 25 26 27 28

The autumnal equinox occurs about the 23rd, marking the start of fall.

Asters are blooming.

Green darner dragonflies are migrating south, one of the few dragonflies that does migrate. Most adults of other species die in the fall.

29 30

Bats that migrate south for the winter are leaving the area.

October

1 2 3 4 5 6 7

Woodchucks are feeding on grass, putting on fat for hibernation.

Dark-eyed juncos are just arriving for the cold months. Slate gray above and white below, they often look for seeds on the ground beneath bird feeders.

8 9 10 11 12 13 14

Bullfrogs, snapping turtles and garter snakes are entering hibernation. The warmer the autumn, the later this will happen.

Fall foliage colors in much of the region are at their peak.

15 16 17 18 19 20 21

Listen for spring peepers calling in the woods on especially warm days.

Moose and deer are in their mating seasons. It is the time of year you're most likely to see a bull or buck as the males are traveling widely to find a mate.

22 23 24 25 26 27 28

The first flurries of snow for the season may be seen about now.

The baby spiders of some species are emerging from eggs. Others wait until spring.

Once a frost occurs, goldenrod starts to disappear from fields and roadsides.

29 30 31

The leaves on some oaks and beeches, although brown, may remain on the trees through the winter.

WESTERN MASSACHUSETTS NATURE CALENDAR

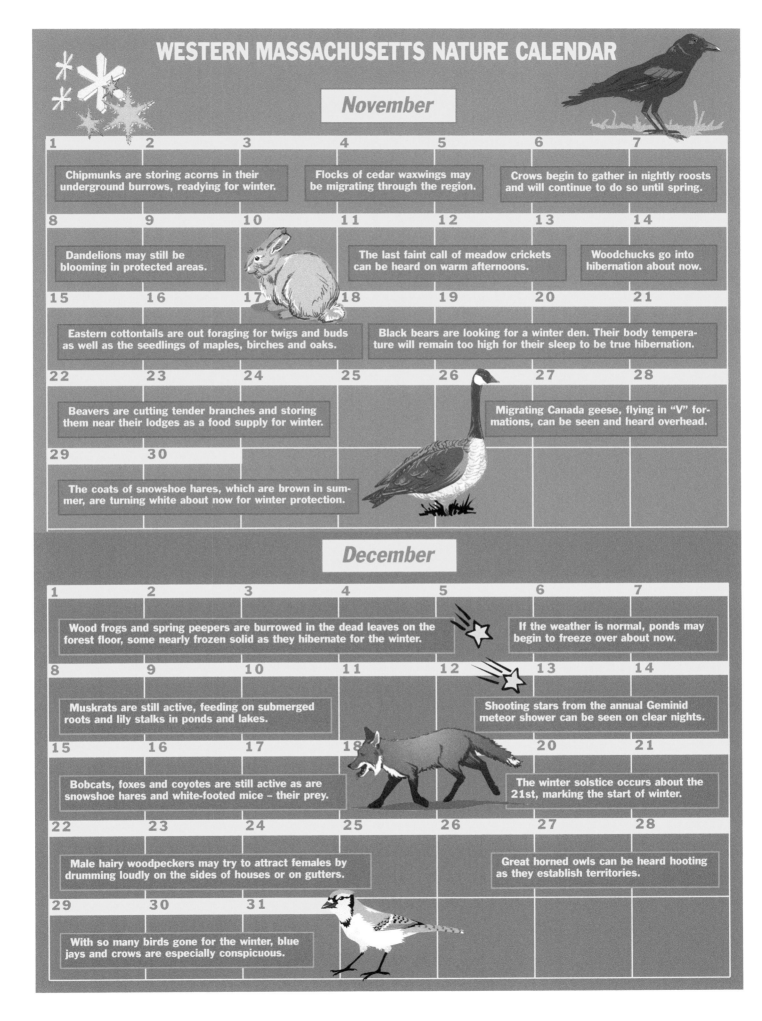

November

1	2	3	4	5	6	7
Chipmunks are storing acorns in their underground burrows, readying for winter.			Flocks of cedar waxwings may be migrating through the region.		Crows begin to gather in nightly roosts and will continue to do so until spring.	

8	9	10	11	12	13	14
Dandelions may still be blooming in protected areas.			The last faint call of meadow crickets can be heard on warm afternoons.		Woodchucks go into hibernation about now.	

15	16	17	18	19	20	21
Eastern cottontails are out foraging for twigs and buds as well as the seedlings of maples, birches and oaks.			Black bears are looking for a winter den. Their body temperature will remain too high for their sleep to be true hibernation.			

22	23	24	25	26	27	28
Beavers are cutting tender branches and storing them near their lodges as a food supply for winter.				Migrating Canada geese, flying in "V" formations, can be seen and heard overhead.		

29	30					
The coats of snowshoe hares, which are brown in summer, are turning white about now for winter protection.						

December

1	2	3	4	5	6	7
Wood frogs and spring peepers are burrowed in the dead leaves on the forest floor, some nearly frozen solid as they hibernate for the winter.					If the weather is normal, ponds may begin to freeze over about now.	

8	9	10	11	12	13	14
Muskrats are still active, feeding on submerged roots and lily stalks in ponds and lakes.					Shooting stars from the annual Geminid meteor shower can be seen on clear nights.	

15	16	17	18	19	20	21
Bobcats, foxes and coyotes are still active as are snowshoe hares and white-footed mice – their prey.					The winter solstice occurs about the 21st, marking the start of winter.	

22	23	24	25	26	27	28
Male hairy woodpeckers may try to attract females by drumming loudly on the sides of houses or on gutters.					Great horned owls can be heard hooting as they establish territories.	

29	30	31				
With so many birds gone for the winter, blue jays and crows are especially conspicuous.						

Peregrine falcon

The Natural History of Western Massachusetts

Published by:
Hampshire House Publishing Co.
8 Nonotuck St.
Florence, Mass. 01062
www.hampshirehousepub.com

Printed in the USA
Updated: Jan. 1, 2016
Copyright © 2015 by Stan Freeman and Mike Nasuti
ISBN: 97809893333-0-6

Facts and figures change, and every other year around Jan. 1, we will update the book, even adding new photos or articles.

Front cover photo: red fox

Some of the material in this book is based on articles by the authors that originally appeared in *The Republican* of Springfield, Mass.

The authors would especially like to thank Mike Williams, Jeff Boettner, the Massachusetts Division of Fisheries and Wildlife, the Connecticut River Watershed Council, the Massachusetts Audubon Society and the New England Wild Flower Society for their help in preparing this book or for the permissions they gave us for material used in it.

If you find what you believe is an error, please notify us by email at hamphouse@comcast.net. The books are printed as they are ordered, which means we can upload a corrected digital file to the printer overnight and the new version will be in print the following day.

Photography credits

All photos are by Stan Freeman unless otherwise noted. A photograph's position on a page is indicated as follows: T = top, C = center, B = bottom, R = right, L = left and A = all photos on page or in the indicated region of page.

Frandy Johnson – 30L; **Holly Schlacter Lowe** – 12T, 12CL, 12C; **Anne Terninko** 32C; **Rob Friedman** 78TR; **Kindra Clineff** 104; **Paul Parent** 107; **Wood Museum of Springfield History** 115BL; **Illinois Department of Natural Resources** – 27TR, 28BL, 28BR, 34B, 37TC; **U.S. Centers for Disease Control** – 41BR, 57CL, 57CR; **U.S. Fish & Wildlife Service** – 23BL, 27 (gray wolf), 27 (red wolf), 30TR, 33B, 33CR, 38BC, 42TR, 55B, 74B, 75, 76TL, 76BR, 123; **U.S. Department of Agriculture** – 61CR; **Library of Congress** – 91B; **Corel** – 2T, 11TL, 13A, 14A, 15TR, 15B, 18T, 21CL (hawk), 23A, 24A, 26B, 27 (western coyote), 29B, 28BR, 28CR, 29B, 31A, 36BL, 40BL, 40BR, 41CR, 66CL, 66CR, 123, back cover CTL; **Shutterstock** – 18BR, 35C, 39, 40BL, 40BR, 47CL, 48T, 50CR, 52TR, 54B, 55TL, 56TR, 57BR, 61TR, 61CL, 64, 67T, 77T, 83R, 92T, 96TR

Coyote howling at the moon

This series highlights the natural history of individual states in the Northeast. We began with a basic book, essentially a collection of articles, and we are attempting to adapt it to each state in the series. So some material in this book, including text, illustrations and photographs, is repeated from book to book in the series.

CPSIA information can be obtained
at www.ICGtesting.com
Printed in the USA
FSHW02n0418080518
47793FS

9 780989 333306